INDUSTRIES
Which Made
BRITAIN TRIUMPH

BRITAIN'S INDUSTRIAL HERITAGE VOLUME 3

written and photographed by
JOHN HANNAVY

First published in 2017

ISBN 978 0 85710 111 2

PiXZ Books
Halsgrove House, Ryelands Business Park, Bagley Road, Wellington, Somerset TA21 9PZ
Tel: 01823 653777
Fax: 01823 216796
email: sales@halsgrove.com

An imprint of Halstar Ltd, part of the Halsgrove group of companies
Information on all Halsgrove titles is available at: www.halsgrove.com

Printed and bound in India by Parksons Graphics

Front cover image: The beautifully preserved 1905 Burrell engine *Edward VII*, on display at the Thursford Collection in Norfolk.

Title page image: Thursford's Victorian Gallopers date from 1896.

Contents page image: A warning notice once found in every steelworks. This example is preserved as part of 'The Big Melt' experience at the Magna Science Centre in the former Templeborough Steelworks in Rotherham. 'Hot Metal' was also the term used to describe early machine typecasting in the printing industry.

My thanks go to the curators of the many museums and heritage sites who have granted me access to their collections and offered valuable advice – they are all listed in the Gazetteer; to Mervyn Gledhill for his recollections of working as a photographer in a float glass factory in the 1960s; to Ben Neale at Wookey Hole for permitting me to photograph him making paper; to Richard Biddulph, Kathryn Carruthers, Helen Hall and Malcolm Jones for the use of their photographs and as ever to my wife Kath for her enduring tolerance and support.

All the modern photographs in this book are © the author except the following – Richard Biddulph/Vintage & Prestige Cars p125 *top right*; Kathryn Carruthers p8 *top left & left*; Grampian Transport Museum p113 *top left & bottom*; Helen Hall p14 *bottom left*; Malcolm Jones p79, all of which are reproduced with thanks.

All Victorian and Edwardian images are © John Hannavy Image Library.

By the same author, also published by PiXZ:
• *Preserved Steam-Powered Machines*
• *Edwardian Mining In Old Postcards*
• *The Once-Ubiquitous Paddle-Steamer*
• *Britain's Industrial Heritage*
• *Our Industrial Past – Britain's Industrial Heritage 2*

CONTENTS

INTRODUCTION

THIS THIRD COLLECTION CELEBRATING Britain's long industrial heritage is, like its two companion volumes, somewhat eclectic in its subjects and content. Like my earlier books, a thematic approach has been used to explore the rich legacy of past generations, and along the way I have explored machinery and processes I had never seen before – from the everyday to the bizarre. I have learned a lot and watched people employ skills I had never even dreamed of.

The output of the golden age of British manufacturing is still all around us – even in the humblest of Victorian buildings, the skills of the engineer, the iron-founder and the craftsman are there to be seen and marvelled at.

There are 'new' heritage sites opening each year, together with ever more industrial steam engines, traction engines and steam locomotives being restored and brought back to life, so the heritage landscape seems to be ever-expanding. There are now many more places to visit than could ever reasonably be covered in a lifetime.

Many of the surviving examples of past industrial technologies are unique, making a visit to see them that bit more special – and also placing on those who tend to them the additional responsibility of fundraising to maintain them for as long as possible into the future. Keeping them operational and safe does not come cheap.

opposite: The steel framework inside the south tower of Tower Bridge in London.

below: Cast-iron columns by Weir & McElroy in celebrated Glasgow architect Alexander 'Greek' Thomson's Saint Vincent Street church which was opened in the city in 1859. John McElroy's Glasgow foundries produced a wide range of castings, from finely detailed work like this, to heavy ironwork for the construction and railway industries. The company worked extensively for Thomson who had earlier designed McElroy's 'Italian Villa' at Cove on the Clyde.

5

above: *Black Prince* preparing to run round the train at Sheringham Station for the return journey to Holt.

top right: The fireman hard at work on BR Class 9F 2-10-0 92203 *Black Prince* at Holt on the North Norfolk Railway.

right: The North Norfolk Railway's Class B12/3 was built for the LNER in 1928 by Beyer-Peacock of Gorton, Manchester.

above right: The Death & Ellwood 'facing lathe' at Dinorwig, the Welsh National Slate Museum, could handle objects up to 7ft in diameter. It was built at the Albert Works in Leicester and was used in the making of wheels and turntables.

As costs mount, that burden increases exponentially. Without the bands of volunteers, the majority of whom work without payment to keep these unique machines operational, our experiences would be much less rich.

One of the many unique examples is illustrated above – the last surviving B12 locomotive from a class which once numbered eighty. Originally designed by the Great Eastern Railway before the Great War, and classed by the GER as S69, this engine comes from an additional batch of ten built in Manchester by Beyer-Peacock of Gorton in the 1920s.

While steam heritage lines continue to prosper, 2015 marked a significant milestone in the story of the steam train, with Abelio ScotRail's announcement that the newly re-opened Borders Railway from Edinburgh Waverley to

Tweedbank would include regular scheduled steam-hauled trains, nearly half a century after Dr Richard Beeching had announced the end of steam on BR metals – the last such service having pulled out of Preston Station on Saturday 3rd August 1968 bound for Liverpool and hauled by Stanier 'Black 5' No.45318.

It is as a direct result of the efforts of those enthusiasts who kept steam alive in the years after Dr Beeching's swingeing changes to the railways that the draw of the steam train still attracts people in their hundreds of thousands two generations later, the majority of them not even born when the fire was dropped on 45318 for the last time by a British Railways' employee.

below left: The 43 metre dish of Manchester University's Lovell Radio Telescope at Jodrell Bank in Cheshire has been at the forefront of radio-astronomy since the 1950s. It tracked the Russian Sputnik 1, the world's first satellite, in October 1957 and was therefore in at the birth of the space age. The giant wheels which allow the dish to tilt were recycled from battle-ship gun turrets.

below: The Jodrell Bank Discovery Centre sets out to explain how radio-astronomy works, and the role it plays in furthering our understanding of our universe, with a range of visual and technical aids. This is yours truly taking a very different sort of 'selfie' on the screen of the Centre's infra-red camera.

Since 1968, steam enthusiasts have had the growing number of heritage lines to enjoy, but only the occasional mainline steam special to look forward to – but to see scheduled steam trains arrive and leave from the platforms in Edinburgh's Waverley Station had just been a dream few thought would ever actually come to pass.

The new services initially operated two days a week in 2015, hauled in

Jodrell Bank infra-red camera

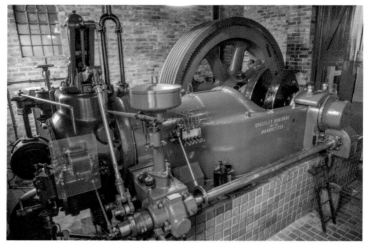

above: A4 60009 *Union of South Africa* at Edinburgh Waverley, top, and the new station at Tweedbank, above, carrying a plaque to mark the opening of the Borders Railway in September 2015.

above right: Said to be the largest single cylinder gas engine ever manufactured by Crossley Brothers of Manchester, this 150hp engine, built in 1915, drove a rod and bar rolling mill in Sheffield. Established in 1867, Crossley engines were used in many factories across the world as well as small electricity generating systems including that which powered the Widnes-Runcorn Transporter Bridge. This engine is now displayed in Sheffield's Kelham Island Museum.

September and October by John Cameron's 1938 Doncaster-built A4 Pacific 60009 *Union of South Africa* with other locomotives planned for the service in the future. For the 2016 roster, 60009 was joined by 46100 *Royal Scot*.

Elsewhere, steam has been kept alive in an increasing number of mills and factories and at the many traction engine rallies which now take place annually across the country.

I began writing and illustrating magazine articles about Britain's architectural and industrial past in the late 1960s and in the decades since then I have watched radical changes take place in what we expect to get from our visits to museums and heritage sites.

Even the media which I use to record and reveal that legacy has changed out of all recognition. In my early days, now nearly fifty years ago, I used a large tripod-mounted camera and, of course, film – and not very fast film at that.

Colour film with an ISO speed of just 125 or 160 was considered 'High Speed', and that severely limited what sort of photography was possible, especially indoors. Yet, when 'High Speed Ektachrome' film was introduced in the late 1960s, we thought it was amazing stuff – hitherto the fastest colour films had been in the range of ISO 50-64, and 35mm Kodachrome was rated at only ISO 25.

Taking photographs inside a stately home, a mill or a factory back then in the late 1960s and '70s required a battery

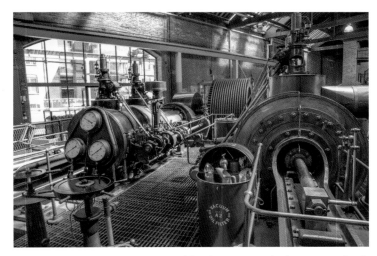

left: The last new steam engine to be installed in a British cotton mill, built by Galloways of Knott Mill, Manchester, for Elm Street Mill in Burnley in 1926, is now displayed in Manchester's Museum of Science & Industry.

below: The casting shed in the workshops at Dinorwig slate-works manufactured everything from rails to locomotive wheels.

of floodlights, or an array of high powered electronic flash units, and it was not unusual for a photographer to spend several hours setting up the lighting necessary to take a single photograph – often on a sheet of 5"x4" colour film.

Today's top-end digital cameras, on the other hand, can

be wound up to speeds in excess of ISO 25,000 without too much loss of quality, and that means that the fascinating detail of dark factory and workshop interiors can be revealed more clearly in photographs than is often possible with the naked eye.

Simply put, pictures are possible today under conditions which were pretty much impossible when I started out professionally.

Where once floodlighting or flash lighting had to be introduced, photo-graphing interiors under natural light today creates a much more pleasing effect.

I marvel at what the technology inside today's cameras enables me to do. And that technology has come along at exactly the right time to

top right: This tandem compound steam engine was built in 1907 by J. & W. McNaught of Rochdale and powered the flannelette sheet looms at R. Barnes & Company's Firgrove Mill in Rochdale. It is displayed in the Power Hall at Manchester's Museum of Science & Industry, a steam enthusiasts' dream. The museum is housed in Liverpool Road Railway Station — the first custom-built station in the world — and the former warehouses and locomotive sheds which were built around it.

right: This 250hp single-cylinder slide-valve horizontal engine, built by Earnshaw & Holt of Rochdale in 1864, powered the looms in A. & W. Law's Durn Mill in Littleborough, Lancashire until the early 1950s. It is also displayed in MOSI's Power Hall where several of the many mill engines are steamed daily for visitors. It powered the looms through spur and bevel gearing rather than the more conventional rope drum and belts. Despite being in England, Durn Mill was a major producer of tartan.

permit us to create images with an immediacy and informality never before possible, and capture the magic of working machinery under prevailing lighting conditions, rather than artificially lit.

In today's heritage culture restoring machinery and getting it back into operation doing what it was originally designed to do is considered a high priority. If it is factory or mill machinery, obviously it stays inside, but if machines were designed for outdoor use, getting them back outside and back to work adds that extra dimension of realism to the visitor experience.

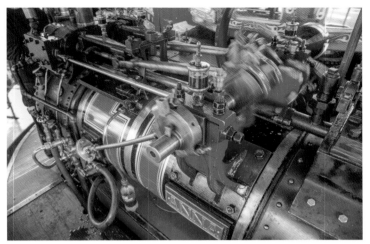

The 2/3hp centre engine which drives the 36ft diameter steam gallopers at Carters Steam Fairs was built by Robert Tidman & Sons of Bishop Bridge Iron Works, Norwich, who in the closing years of the nineteenth century briefly rivalled Savages in the production of steam fairground rides. The company was established in 1883, and ceased operations in 1925. This engine is believed to date from c.1892 and its boiler carries the nameplate of A.J. & R.K. Bicknell of Haslemere after repairs in 1907. It was returned to steam by the Carters in 1977.

During a discussion about traction engines, a colleague told me he hated to see them 'stuffed and mounted' in museums – understandably preferring to enjoy them in steam and working as hard as they were designed to work.

There is, of course, a place for both, as not everyone – surprisingly in the opinion of diehard enthusiasts such as myself – gets high on that wonderfully addictive smell which comes from the intoxicating mixture of coal smoke, hot oil and steam.

Most visitors to heritage sites today, however, expect much more than just the opportunity to look at static exhibits. The museums of my childhood were undoubtedly places of wonder then, but like everything else, they were products of a much more formal age, and most have moved with the times, seeking that delicate balance between fulfilling their educational briefs and attracting and engaging with visitors.

The balance *is* delicate, because it must be all too easy to overstep the mark and become too like a theme park. Luckily, the majority of sites get the balance about right.

We do not now simply expect to see machines doing what they were built to do – in addition to their sheer spectacle, we demand much more in the way of information and interpretation so that we can establish a context within which to explore and understand what we are seeing. Perhaps nowhere does that better than the annual spectacle which is

right: The 1876 horizontal duplex steam colliery winding engine by Davy Brothers of Sheffield, preserved at Capstone Colliery, the National Mining Museum England at Overton, Wakefield.

below: Detail of an elaborate four column single cylinder beam engine with a 24ins x 36ins cylinder, probably dating from the late 1830s. It was manufactured by Peel, Williams & Peel, engineers and iron founders of Manchester at their Soho Ironworks in Ancoats. The original purchaser of the engine is unknown, but it was certainly already secondhand when acquired by Best & Lloyd, brass-founders and lighting manufacturers of Smethwick in the second half of the nineteenth century. Best & Lloyd, established in Birmingham in 1840, are still leading lighting manufacturers today. The engine has since been relocated to Blists Hill Victorian Town in Shropshire. Peel, Williams & Peel's foundry was demolished in 1976, and the site now lies beneath Manchester's Metrolink tram line to Ashton-under-Lyne.

the Great Dorset Steam Fair. There we are confronted by the sheer diversity of the application of steam power, from sawing and farming, to road engines and the fairground rides which light up the evening sky.

The engineering which went into a roundabout's centre engine was no different except in scale, to that which powered a mill engine or a steamship, and the fusion of technical and artistic skills evident in the roundabout itself – including those of the wood carvers and the painters who created and decorated the ornate Gallopers – is awesome. Entertaining our predecessors required the same engineering ingenuity as

left: Now in the Manchester Museum of Science & Industry, this 1905 Rolls Royce was only the 12th car built by the company at their factory in Hulme, Manchester. Originally a 4-seater, it was used by Henry Royce himself before being fitted with its current Barker body and sold in December 1906.

below: The iconic paddle steamer PS *Waverley* — the last sea-going paddle steamer in the world — passes the Tower of London in October 2015, crowded with passengers. Eight hundred and fifty years separate these two fine examples of British engineering skill — the White Tower was completed in 1097, PS *Waverley* in 1947.

providing their food, weaving their fabrics, and transporting their everyday needs around the country. It was a challenge which brought together the engineer and artist.

As my travels with my cameras have taken me around the world, I have never failed to be amazed at the ingenuity of past generations, and equally, at the increasing number of museums and preservation groups which have been set up to celebrate that ingenuity.

British-built machinery was world-renowned throughout the nineteenth century and well into the twentieth century as

right and below right: Britain supplied much of the equipment for the 1911-built Lake Wakatipu steamer TSS *Earnslaw*, built by McGregors of Dunedin in New Zealand — the steering mechanism from Thomas Reid & Sons of Paisley, the winches from Emerson Walker & Thompson Brothers Ltd of Gateshead, capstans from a foundry in Stockton, and the bridge telegraph from Chadburn's of Liverpool.

below: This boiler by Jones, Burton & Co of Liverpool has powered the steam engines in a sugar cane and rum factory in Porto Da Cruz, Madeira, since 1927, but it is now used only as the backup.

being completely reliable and precision engineered to provide long service.

A significant proportion of the country's industrial output was exported, not only keeping an ever-expanding manufacturing workforce employed, but also the many shipping companies who exported it across the globe – on ships built in British yards, of course.

Working examples of our rich heritage can still be found all over the world, in places as far afield as India, Australia and New Zealand testifying both to

There were once 42 giant 'hammerhead' cranes in operation around the world, mostly built by Sir William Arrol. Today there are just a dozen. Illustrated here are, *above left* the Titan in Greenock's James Watt Dock and, above, Glasgow's Finnieston Crane. The Australian Navy's 1951 Arrol Titan in Sydney, *left* — the third last to be built and rarely used since 1991 — was demolished in 2014.

the uncompromising standards of which British manufacturers were proud and to the reputation of British-built products. Today, sadly, our trade in manufactured goods is almost all in reverse, importing huge tonnages of goods from the same countries to which we once regularly exported.

As with all these books, I am indebted to the generosity of the many working sites and industrial museums in Britain and elsewhere, and their bands of experts and volunteers, who have welcomed me and given me access to their collections and their expertise, and allowed me freedom of movement with my cameras.

Without them my travels and explorations would have been much less rewarding and I would have many fewer stories to tell.

John Hannavy 2017

above: The retro styling of India's hugely popular Hindustan Ambassador, the locally produced version of the 1954 Morris Oxford Mk.III, remained virtually unchanged from its launch in 1957 until production of the car eventually ceased in 2014

PAPER AND PRINT

WITHOUT PAPER, WHERE WOULD WE BE? Well, this book – and the millions of others which have been written over the centuries – would not exist for a start. Paper is such a core component of our everyday lives, that it is not an overstatement to say that our civilised world depends on it.

The paper and print industries today are highly automated, making possible the production of books, magazines and all sorts of packaging of outstanding quality, all printed on durable materials from sustainable sources.

Paper and print production have both undergone a revolution in recent years and are now virtually unrecognisable from the labour-intensive industries of less than a century ago.

Modern 4-colour printing presses are huge and very fast, helping to keep the cost of print affordable but the widespread availability of print could never have happened without the mechanisation of paper-making – often described as paper's own 'Industrial Revolution'.

While paper was probably made in China as early as 105AD, the first recorded instance of it being manufactured

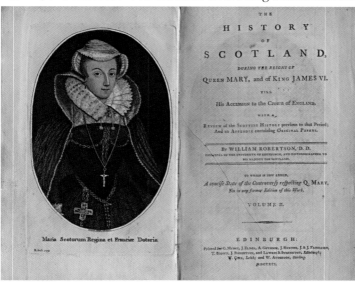

Maria Scotorum Regina et Franciæ Dotaria

THE
HISTORY
OF
SCOTLAND,
DURING THE REIGNS OF
QUEEN MARY, and of KING JAMES VI.
TILL
His Accession to the Crown of ENGLAND.
WITH A,
REVIEW of the SCOTTISH HISTORY previous to that Period;
And an APPENDIX containing ORIGINAL PAPERS.
By WILLIAM ROBERTSON, D.D.
PRINCIPAL OF THE UNIVERSITY OF EDINBURGH, AND HISTORIOGRAPHER TO
HIS MAJESTY FOR SCOTLAND.
TO WHICH IS NOW ADDED,
A concise State of the Controversy respecting Q. MARY,
Not in any former Edition of this Work.
VOLUME II.
EDINBURGH:
Printed for G. Mudie, J. Elder, A. Guthrie, J. Hunter, J. & J. Fairbairn,
T. Brown, J. Robertson, and Lawrie & Symington, Edinburgh;
W. Coke, Leith; and W. Auchison, Stirling.
MDCCXCI.

opposite page: The late-Victorian rag boiler in the Wookey Hole Paper Mill in Somerset. When paper was made from cotton rag, Wookey Hole Mill took all the cotton waste from a shirt manufacturer in nearby Taunton. It was then cut into small pieces and boiled up to clean it before being transferred to the beating machine which broke down the fibres into the cotton pulp which was the basic material for papermaking.

below left: The frontispiece of Dr William Robertson's 1791 *History of Scotland during the Reigns of Queen Mary, and of King James VI*, printed in Edinburgh on hand-made sheets of cotton rag paper. The impression of the wire mesh mould on which the paper was made *(see example on page 20)* can still be seen on the right-hand page. With every single letter typeset by hand — a hugely labour-intensive task — and low sales volumes due to limited literacy, books at that time carried a premium price.

right: Many early British mills would have used water-powered wooden rag-stampers to break down the fibres in the cotton waste. These early eighteenth-century examples are in the Milano Mill in Amalfi, Italy. This design was widely used across Europe for centuries.

above: The water or wind-powered 'Hollander Beater' was invented in Holland in the middle of the seventeenth century, but took more than half a century to be widely used in papermills, manufacturers preferring the tried and tested rag-stampers. This Hollander, also in the Milano Mill in Amalfi, was installed in November 1745.

in Britain is not until almost 1400 years later when John Tate started making paper at his mill on the River Beane near Hertford in the 1490s. In those days, sheets of paper were made individually by hand, a labour-intensive process reflected in a premium price tag. And yet access to paper so changed the world that thousands of mills were built over the ensuing centuries, some employing the entire adult population of the villages which grew up alongside them.

John Tate's papers were instantly recognisable as they bore a watermark, created by pressing a wire stamp into the wet paper – a method still used today, albeit by machines on to vast rolls of paper using a wire mesh 'Dandy Roll' rather than on to each individual sheet.

A key requirement in papermaking is water, so early mills were built alongside rivers. When mechanisation started to appear in the late seventeenth century, larger mills were set up beside fast moving streams, large waterwheels powering both the rag-beaters and the earliest of papermaking machines. While no examples survive of British water-powered paper mills, the fascinating Milano Mill in Amalfi, Italy – where paper was made from the thirteenth century right up until 1969 – contains fine examples of the sort of equipment which would have been in seventeenth and eighteenth century British mills.

Making paper involved the shredding and beating of cotton rag – or raw cotton itself – to completely break down the fibres. That process was labour-intensive and very slow.

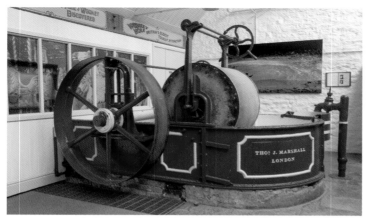

left: The cotton rag shredder at Wookey Hole was purchased from Thomas J. Marshall of Bishopsgate-Without in London and installed in the rebuilt mill in 1848. Marshalls exhibited paper-making machines and water-marking dandy rolls in 1862 at the International Exhibition in London. Papers produced at Wookey Hole were of fine quality and high durability, and proved very popular with the printers of banknotes.

Even when water-powered stampers were introduced in the early eighteenth century, it took 24 hours to break the fibres down sufficiently. By the mid-eighteenth century, rag-stampers were being replaced by the toothed 'Hollander Beater' – which could be powered by water or wind – reducing the time to break down the rag fibres to about four hours.

The pulverised cotton was mixed with water until a slurry – known as 'stuff', 'half-stuff' or 'stock' – of the right consistency was achieved and this was kept moving in a tank

below: The paper-making cycle at Wookey Hole worked clockwise from the pulp tank at the back of the picture. The hydrated pulp was fed into the tank at the right where the two papermakers – the Vatman and his assistant, the Coucher – worked. The Vatman scooped the pulp on to the wire mesh moulds and passed them, dripping, to the Coucher who transferred them to the 'couch'– the board on which each sheet of prepared pulp was added to the pile of sheets and felts. The couch was then run on rails along to the giant press in the foreground where much of the water was squeezed out.

right: Pulped recycled paper waste at Frogmore ready to be made into new paper is mixed with water in a large cauldron.

below: An early nineteenth century wire mesh mould, showing the die which impressed the watermark. On machines the water-mark was introduced using a 'dandy roll', invented in 1826 by Dartford mill-owner John Marshall.

bottom: Ben Neale demonstrating paper-making at Wookey Hole Paper Mill in Somerset, where paper was first made in the mid-seventeenth century.

to ensure the pulp didn't settle. To make a sheet of paper, it was scooped up on to a wire mesh mould and allowed to drain. The mould was then upturned on to a sheet of felt, on top of which was placed another felt, another sheet of paper, and so on until there was a thick stack or 'post'. The water content was still very high, each 'sheet' just a thick even layer of pulp. The 'post' was then placed into a powerful press which forced out as much of the water as possible.

left: Frogmore Paper Mill in Hertfordshire. There had been a water-powered flour mill on the site since the thirteenth century, but production of paper — handmade at first — started in the second half of the eighteenth century. The brothers Henry and Sealy Fourdrinier installed the first continuous paper-making machine which bears their name in 1803. Fourdrinier machines were used through-out the world and Frogmore's 1895 machine made paper continuously from 1906 until 2009.

By then, each sheet of paper was stable enough to be handled, but it still had a water content of around 50%. It required slow drying over several days before it was ready for trimming and preparing for sale and use.

The earliest papers were nothing like the materials we are used to today. Their texture was akin to blotting paper and they were highly absorbent and likely to fall apart when damp. To counter that, starch or 'size' was added to give the paper greater strength and make it possible to write on the surface without the ink diffusing into the material. Each manufacturer had his own ideas about how much size should be applied, so each paper had unique properties.

To make papers whiter, bleach was added – but too much bleach made it less stable and shortened its life. Unbleached papers were much more durable but were creamy in colour.

In the nineteenth century, with the advent of photography – and the paper negative in particular – the watermark became the bane of the photographer's life as he or she sought out sheets with the watermark in a position which would not appear in the photograph.

James Whatman & Son of Maidstone in Kent had been pioneers of 'wove paper' – a smooth writing paper – in the 1740s and by the middle of the nineteenth century they produced a wide range of cotton rag-based papers. Their *Whatman's Turkey Mill* papers were very popular with both watercolour artists and commercial printers as well as photographers.

right: The liquefied pulp is introduced to the moving wire belt on the Fourdrinier machine. As it moves along, the water is drained out of the paper through the wire mesh, the paper quickly becoming self-supporting.

middle and bottom: This small Fourdrinier machine still manufactures specialist papers at Frogmore. It was originally built in 1902 for the Manchester College of Science and Technology — now part of the University of Manchester — as a testing and teaching machine, later spending some years at Bury College before being rebuilt at Frogmore. While now electrically-driven, steam is still used to heat the drying rollers.

opposite page top: The large 1895-built Fourdrinier machine at Frogmore Mill was decommissioned in 2009, but there are plans to restore it.

opposite bottom: The last of several steam engines to power the 1895 paper-making machine was a 1956-built 130hp inverted vertical two-cylinder duplex fully enclosed engine by Ashworth & Parker of Bury.

Hertfordshire has a special place in the pantheon of British paper-making and one important date in that history is 1803 when the first mechanised paper-making machine was installed at Frogmore Mill by two successful London stationers, the brothers Henry and Sealy Fourdrinier.

Frogmore still makes paper today and is the oldest mechanised paper mill in the world still doing what it was built to do more than two centuries ago.

While the mill's large 1895-built paper-making machine and its 1956 steam engine await restoration, a small Fourdrinier machine – built as a teaching aid in 1902 – can still be seen in operation, making a range of recycled papers whenever the Apsley Paper Trail is open.

right: James Bertram & Son Ltd. was established in 1854 manufacturing paper-making machinery and advertised their Fourdrinier machines in the trade press well into the 1950s. Despite being built sixty years after the Frogmore machine, the one advertised here is remarkably similar in appearance.

below: A mid-nineteenth century woodcut of what a Renaissance print shop might have looked like.

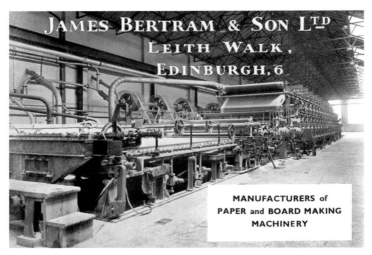

MANUFACTURERS of
PAPER and BOARD MAKING
MACHINERY

Today, papers are generally made out of cellulose from wood pulp to which is added a precise amount of bleach to whiten it, and a filler to create the smooth surface we need if we are to write or print on it. The most common filler is kaolin, or china clay – much of it from clay pits around St. Austell in Cornwall – the same basic material which is used to make porcelain.

Most paper today is made on huge machines, some as long as a football pitch and operating at speeds of 60mph producing rolls of paper weighing upwards of 20 tons.

The first machine to be set up in Britain was based on a 1798 design by French engineer Louis-Nicholas Robert, but as France was in turmoil after the Revolution, he realised that the potential for development there was limited.

Brought to Britain by John Gamble in 1801, Robert's machine clearly impressed the Fourdriniers, despite basic reliability problems, as Robert had demonstrated its ability to make lengths of wallpaper cheaply and efficiently. Wallpaper's high price had hitherto meant it was affordable only by the rich.

far left: A replica of a fifteenth century Gutenberg Press in the Museum of Science & Industry in Manchester.

left: Columbian presses were first introduced around 1813 and can still be found in the fine print workshops of art colleges and universities today. This example is also displayed in the Museum of Science & Industry in Manchester. The heavy eagle served two purposes — firstly it was the counter-weight which raised the platen after the impression had been made, and secondly it was intended to make a Columbian Press visually distinctive and, according to its designer John Clymer, unforgettable.

Modified by engineer Bryan Donkin at his works in Bermondsey, the first successful machine was installed in 1804 at Frogmore Mill in Hertfordshire, becoming known as the Fourdrinier Machine. The machine used steam power to drive it and the same steam heated the rollers which dried the paper. Steam heat is still used on many machines in the drying process today.

Donkin went on to work in the 1820s with Charles Babbage in realising Babbage's idea for his *Difference Engine*, with Marc and Isambard Brunel supplying efficient pumping engines for use during the boring of the Thames Tunnel, and in the development in the 1840s of valve systems for the gas industry. For his work on the papermaking machine, Donkin was later awarded a Gold Medal at the 1851 Great Exhibition in Hyde Park.

At around the same time Polish-born Matthias Koops set up Neckinger Mill in Bermondsey making paper from recycled waste and announced he was producing 700 reams a week of clean and white paper from recycled written and printed paper which would otherwise have been thrown away. Recycling is clearly nothing new.

Frogmore's 1895 Fourdrinier Machine was built by James Bertram & Sons Ltd of Leith Walk, Edinburgh for the Kinleith Paper Mill in Currie on the outskirts of the city. It was purchased second-hand from Bertrams in 1906 for £800 and

top: The typesetter assembled the text by hand using individual wooden or lead letter forms. These were then assembled in a wooden frame known as a 'chase' and fixed in place by lockable 'quoins' before being mounted on either a flat-bed or platen press for printing.

above: The Imperial Press was built by Cope, Sherwin & Company in Shoreditch, London in the early nineteenth century. Richard Cope is said to have worked with Clymer on the Columbian press and also designed the 'Albion' press.

installed at Frogmore in 1907 along with a new steam engine.

As it stands today, it includes parts made by James Milne and Son of Milton House Works, Edinburgh and Black Clawson of Newport. How much of the original machine survives has not been determined.

With the increasing availability of more affordable paper, demand for affordable print was just a step behind it.

Moveable type was the invention which made the mass production of printed material possible. It was not invented by Johannes Gutenberg in Germany in the fifteenth century as popularly believed, but he did refine the system and popularise it with the production of *The Gutenberg Bible* in 1455. The technique had been known in the Far East since the late fourteenth century.

Gutenberg did, however, pioneer the use of oil-based inks – which vastly improved the durability of printed texts – and the flat-bed printing press which became the most widely-used means of print production across the world.

Indeed the basic design of Gutenberg's press changed very little over the following centuries, and when they started to be made of iron rather than wood – one of the first being George Clymer's 'Washington Press' in 1834 – the most notable difference was the replacement of the wooden screw with a system of compound levers to press the type on to the paper.

Cylinder presses first appeared at the beginning of the nineteenth century, the issue of *The Times* for 29 November 1814 proudly proclaiming that it has been 'printed by steam power'. The press on which the paper was printed was capable of 1100 sheets per hour – more than four times that which could be achieved with a hand press. Initially it only printed one side of each sheet at a time.

Two centuries later, a modern newspaper press can print around half a million sheets per hour, printed in colour.

The ability to set up individual words in re-usable wood or metal letters revolutionised communication and helped create the educated world which we enjoy today.

The type was usually stored in two wooden drawers or 'cases', partitioned to create a dedicated space for each letter of the alphabet. They were kept one above the other – with capital letters in the top one – thus introducing the terms 'upper-case' and 'lower-case' which we still use to describe letterforms today.

The 'upper case' drawer was divided into ninety-eight compartments, for capital letters of different sizes, while the lower-case drawer had fifty-three. These were not all the same size – their capacity dictated by the frequency with which particular letters appeared in the English language.

Nor was the distribution of the letters arranged alphabetically – the compartments containing the most frequently used letters were grouped at the right-hand side of the tray, closest to the typesetter's right hand.

above left: The type for a Music-Hall poster set up on one of a collection of period Adana platen presses of all sizes displayed in Frogmore Paper Mill.

above: One of the most popular platen presses in small printing works was the Heidelberg – the first models being treddle-powered. Introduced in 1958, the 'Original Heidelberg' press was available in two sizes – 10"x15" and 13"x 18". This example is also displayed at Frogmore. Heidelberg is still a leading manufacturer today.

above: A Linotype machine from the 1960s – the keyboard and mechanics, left, and the crucible for the molten lead, right.

below: The cast plate ready for printing the front page of a 1972 newspaper.

As demand for print grew exponentially, the ability to compose and set type much more quickly became of paramount importance, resulting in some highly ingenious and increasingly complex machines.

The first mechanical typesetting machine was developed by the American William Church in 1822 and used conventional individual lead letters pre-loaded into the machine. It did speed up typesetting but not by a significant amount. Sixty years would pass before a faster and more sophisticated system was developed

The real speed boost came along in 1885 when Ottmar Mergenthaler patented his 'slug-casting' machine in which completed lines of text were cast in lead using type matrices rather than by the manual or mechanical assembly of individual letters.

Improvements to his idea led to the development of the Linotype machine which achieved world-wide popularity and became, in its many forms, the standard in newspaper printing works.

Other rival type casting systems were introduced around the same period – amongst them the Typograph and Monotype systems – but the versatility of the Linotype soon assured its ascendancy. Whereas the Monotype had separate keyboard and caster, with the Linotype the entire typing and casting process was carried out in a single unit.

All these systems were for the production of print using the letterpress process, but alongside letterpress, from the second half of the nineteenth century, there was also gravure and later photogravure. Photogravure was developed in 1878 by Czech painter Karel Klíč, who built on Henry Fox Talbot's research from the 1850s. Gravure uses an etched printing plate and is capable of producing exceptional quality. It is still used for very fine colour reproduction.

By the early years of the twentieth century, fine detail, especially with photographs, was made possible using offset lithography. With offset printing, the ink image is transferred from a printing plate to the rubber rollers of the printing press before being transferred once more on to the paper. Since the 1970s newspaper production has been by 'offset litho', combining high quality with high printing speeds.

With the adoption of litho as the industry standard, Linotype machines were consigned to museums – complex mechanical dinosaurs far removed from the computer-based digital systems on which the industry depends today.

Along with the passing of the labour-intensive pre-press stages in print production went dozens of different skills and tens of thousands of jobs. They were replaced by the seemingly almost 'instant' production of finished pages using modern desktop publishing systems.

Had the production of a book like this been possible little more than sixty years ago, many people would have played key roles in preparing the text and the photographs for the printers. For this book, almost all of that pre-press work was done by the author on his computer.

below: The author supervising the printing of his 2015 book *The Victorian Photographs of Dr Thomas Keith and John Forbes White* on a modern Heidelberg 4-colour press at the Gomer Press in Llandysul, south-west Wales.

29

THE FARMING INDUSTRY

SOME THINGS PASS INTO HISTORY almost without us noticing, and the passing of some traditions may not be recognised by most of us for years – until we stumble upon a scene which reminds us of the way things used to be.

Some years ago, when walking in the Dorset countryside, I came across a field with stooks of corn sheaves in long rows drying in the warm autumn air – and realised that was something I had rarely seen since I helped out on a farm as a boy in the early 1960s. The ubiquitous combine harvester had rendered such farming traditions unnecessary.

A century earlier, the prophets of doom had said the same thing about the advent of steam machinery on the farm – and that turned out to be to the detriment of both horses and men, with one pair of steam ploughing engines being able to do in a matter of hours what would have taken several days with a pair of heavy horses.

Earlier still, in 1830, unrest amongst agricultural workers about the increasing mechanisation of their industry led to what became known as the Swing Riots, which started in Kent – so-called after a non-existent Captain Swing who was the figurative leader of the rebellion. The violence was directed partly towards landowners and the system of tithes, but also against the introduction of mechanical threshing machines. Those early machines were driven by two horses,

above and opposite page: Thorpeness Mill was originally built as a corn mill in the village of Aldringham in Suffolk in the early years of the nineteenth century. It was dismantled in 1922 and re-erected the following year on its present site and converted for use as a water pump. The solid post of the original mill was replaced by a hollow one, through which ran the pumping mechanism. Until 1940 it raised water to the nearby 'House in the Clouds' – a disguised water tank – which provided the village's supply.

left: Harvesting a cornfield as part of the 'Yesterday's Farming' event in Somerset. The tractor is a 1938 Case Model RC, one of only five of this wide front axle version to be imported from the USA.

each replacing perhaps a dozen workers with flails.

The introduction of mechanical horse-drawn reapers had a similar impact – one machine doing the work of a dozen men with scythes.

Before the Swing Riots, the much more widely-remembered Tolpuddle Martyrs – a group of Dorset farm labourers – had been sentenced to deportation for forming an illegal trade union to fight for a living wage – illegal because they had sworn an oath of allegiance to their common cause.

While farm workers were demanding a wage of around ten shillings a week in 1824, the Tolpuddle men had seen theirs reduced to seven shillings (35p) with a further threatened reduction to six shillings. So rising food prices in the early nineteenth century were certainly not the result of a profligate wage structure.

Extrapolated from the 1831 Census, it is estimated that around 28% of Britain's population – that's around 5 million people – worked on the land. A century years later, that had dipped to just over a million. By 1970, it was a little over half a million – and a quarter of them were part time or seasonal – and it is even less today.

Steam engines were in use for ploughing fields on larger farms by the 1850s, and in widespread use by the 1880s. Initially these engines were stationary, operating a cable-hauled plough which, while still requiring someone to control it – and an engineer to operate the engine – considerably speeded up the ploughing itself. But it marked the end of the line for tens of thousands of farm labourers.

A knowledge of natural things such as planting seed, feeding horses and being able to control a plough or a pair of horses, was no longer enough. While the basic horse-drawn plough turned over one furrow at a time, powerful mechanical monsters could do up to eight.

In the white heat of Victorian technology, the farmer not only needed to be able to afford the engines, he had to be capable of operating and maintaining them. The farmer-engineer now required considerable mechanical as well as agricultural skills.

Wiltshire-born engineer John Fowler, whose Leeds-based company became a market leader and whose agricultural engines still grace many steam rallies today, was one of the first on the scene with these machines.

His first successful steam plough – his second design, as the first in 1852 had proved unsuccessful – was demonstrated at the Royal Agricultural Society of England meeting in Lincoln in 1854.

The farm worker's life remained a hard and ill-paid one throughout the nineteenth century, a century which saw an estimated three million men and women leave the land and migrate to better paid jobs – but worse living conditions – in the industrialised towns and cities.

And yet interestingly, the emerging Edwardian postcard industry in the early twentieth century almost ignored the

opposite page: Long after steam became an everyday feature of farming life, postcard publishers continued to publish cards which celebrated the importance of the horse on the farm. While most postcards were marketed to a public seeking traditional images, pioneers such as the International Harvester Company of America saw the postcard as an advertising tool. They used it to promote their mechanised horse-drawn binder, seen working a field near Stirling c.1904 in the third postcard.

below: A detail from a postcard c.1906, captioned 'Threshing Oats'. Relatively few postcards were produced in the Edwardian era showing steam engines at work on the farm.

right: Steam ploughing with a Fowler four-share plough and a pair of Fowler ploughing engines at the Great Dorset Steam Fair.

middle: Steam ploughing trials at Farningham in Kent in 1862, as illustrated in the *Illustrated London News*. In the illustration, the Fowler plough is shown with just three plough shares.

below: Starting the long job of ploughing a recently harvested cornfield with a pair of Shire horses and a single share plough. Such traditions were already being taken over by mechanised systems more than a century and a half ago.

new 'modern' steam-driven farm, flooding the market instead with nostalgic postcard views which celebrated the traditional labour-intensive methods of ploughing and harvesting using people and horses.

Such cards usually focused on smaller and less mechanised family-owned farms, but tapping into the romance of long established tradition was clearly already a feature of every-day life.

While postcard publishers cele-brated the new technology with numerous series on the latest steam locomotives, relatively few steam ploughing engines and steam threshers – or 'thrashers' as they were then often known – were featured. The few which do give a rare glimpse of a time when horses and machines jointly provided the motive power on farms.

When Queen Victoria came to the throne in 1837, Britain's population was a little over 18.5 million. By the end of her reign, that had almost doubled to just under 37 million. Today,

Harrowing with a 1919 10nhp Fowler K7 Ploughing Engine at the top of the hill, *above*, and *Margaret*, an 1870-built 12nhp Fowler engine at the bottom, *below*. Beyond, a pair of engines work the plough.

below: The first trials of a plough designed by the Earl of Dunmore were reported in *The Graphic* magazine in April 1871. In the illustration, his plough is being hauled by a vertical-boilered steam engine designed by Edinburgh-based engineer Robert William Thomson. *The Scotsman* reported that 'Mr. Thomson's road steamer has effected quite a revolution in agriculture', while *The Engineer* noted that it would enable farmers to get rid of all their horses as 'it can fetch its own fuel and water and it can be employed in ploughing, reaping and mowing, in carrying manure, and taking produce to market.' The engine was fitted with solid rubber tyres — despite the fact that Thomson had invented the pneumatic tyre and patented it in 1846 when he was just twenty-three years old. The engine, however, was too heavy and failed to live up to its expectations.

the United Kingdom is home to more than 63 million people. Clearly, a farming industry which could barely feed the population in 1837 could not stand still.

Increasing agricultural output over the past 180 years has been one of the key factors – along with better sanitation and health care – which has seen average life expectancy rise from 41 in 1841 into the 80s today.

Mechanisation, disease resistant crops with much greater yields per acre and better animal husbandry, together with advances in fertilisers, have all contributed to the intensive and highly productive agricultural industry of today.

The mechanisation of farming has continually and radically changed the British landscape over the past two hundred years as larger fields proved easier to plough, easier to harvest, and more productive. The patchwork pattern of small fields which once typified the landscape is long gone.

The first steam-powered machines to be introduced on to Britain's farms can be traced back to the very early years of the nineteenth century – simple low pressure beam engines used for land drainage and built to designs which James Watt and Thomas Newcomen would still have readily recognised.

Although a cable-hauled ploughing engine had been demonstrated – not very successfully – in the early 1830s, the use of more sophisticated and versatile engines really started

LORD DUNMORE'S NEW STEAM-PLOUGH.

about a decade later, the primary aim of their introduction being to reduce not only the number of labourers required, but also the number of horses farmers had to own, and counter the rising costs of feeding them – the horses, that is.

In that respect, the drive towards the mechanisation of every possible aspect of farming echoed the earlier rush to mechanise everything from heavy manufacturing industries to spinning and weaving.

Experience in mills and factories had already, proved that the use of steam power had hugely increased output and lowered both wages and operating costs, the engines paying for themselves relatively quickly.

Within ten years, numerous makers had entered the agricultural market, with ploughing engines and other portable engines being regularly displayed at agricultural fairs across the country.

The roots of the more advanced technology which drove these developments had actually been pioneered half a century earlier, most notably the Cornish boiler with its internal fire tube running the length of the interior and thus heating the water much more efficiently. Cornish boilers were

above left: James Ransome, of Ransomes, Sims & Jefferies of Ipswich was one of the earliest manufacturers of engines. This 1912-built 7nhp single-cylinder general purpose engine carries maker's number 25542.

above: The steering mechanism on most traction engines uses a worm gear system to convert the rotation of the steering wheel, via a chain drive, to steer the front wheels. This is a 1929-built Clayton & Shuttleworth single-cylinder engine, Works No.49105.

This 10/12hp portable engine, built between 1880 and 1900 by Ruston, Proctor & Co. Ltd of Lincoln, was exported to France and sold on by Victor Saelen of Lomme-lez-Lille. The Saelen company was established in 1880 as a manufacturer of farm machinery and was one of the first to build steam-powered threshing machines in France later that decade. The engine is now displayed in the Musée Agricole & Automobile de Salviac in the Lot département in south-west France. Ruston, Proctor & Company was established in 1857 as a manufacturer of farm machinery — including portable engines and steam tractors. A number of them were exported, and although now relatively rare, examples can also be found in preservation across Europe and as far afield as Australia.

left: This 1930 6nhp general purpose traction engine, built by Wallis & Steevens of Basingstoke and now known as *East Lothian Star*, is seen here coupled to a saw bench.

below left: The business end of the saw bench with *East Lothian Star* behind and an ever-changing crowd of onlookers.

bottom: A 1929 Fowler 10nhp compound steam crane, known as *Wolverhampton Wanderer* doing the heavy lifting for a sawing demonstration. The crane was sold new to John Thompson of Ettingshall, Wolverhampton, and used to deliver and install Lancashire boilers all over the country. After 1948 it was relegated to doing general lifting work around the company's stock yard. The vehicle itself weighs in at 23 tons and has a lifting capacity of 10 tons.

top: A 1903 Foden threshing machine at work. Belt-driven from a steam engine or tractor, these machines first appeared in the late eighteenth century and were used for around 175 years until largely superseded by combine harvesters in the 1950s. The threshing machine was one of the triggers which instigated the 'Swing Riots' in the 1830s. The earliest horse-powered threshing machine is believed to have been built by Scottish engineer Andrew Meikle in the mid 1780s.

middle: If the straw was to be used for thatching, the threshing machine had an extra unit fitted which sorted, bundled and tied it into bunches known as 'wadds' and 'nitches', ready for the thatcher to store over winter. This thresher was built by William Foster of Lincoln whose other claim to fame is that he built the world's first military tank.

bottom: *The Hamster*, a 1980-built replica of a Wallis & Steevens 3-ton light tractor, photographed at work powering a threshing machine at the Great Dorset Steam Fair in 2016.

fitted horizontally in the engine rather than vertically, and their much stronger design enabled higher steam pressure to be raised and maintained.

When the single internal tube of the Cornish boiler was replaced by multiple tubes in the 1830s the efficiency of the engine was further increased. That innovation, widely referred to as the locomotive boiler, was used in portable farm engines, traction engines, fairground rides and marine engines as well as the many designs of steam locomotives which drove the railways for a century and a quarter.

One of the first builders of high pressure portable engines was Ipswich engineer James Ransome in the early 1840s. Other early designs came from Marshalls of Gainsborough, Clayton & Shuttleworth, Charles Burrell of Thetford, and many of the other famous names which are still familiar to every steam enthusiast today.

The agricultural steam engine became a true workhorse, adaptable to a variety of roles and able to drive everything on the farm from pulling ploughs to driving threshing machines, sawmills and a host of other equipment. Steam drove what was, undoubtedly, farming's industrial revolution, changing the nature of life on the land forever.

Marshalls – who had started manufacturing steam road engines at their Britannia Works in Gainsborough as early as 1849 – would, in time, become one of the first of the engine manufacturers to recognise that the future of agricultural machinery lay in diesel rather than steam, developing the first of their range of basic but powerful tractors in 1900.

below: A Powell baler, driven by 1919 5nhp Burrell Road Locomotive *Lord Fisher of Lambeth*. This engine was purchased new from the Burrell's stand at the Royal Dairy Show in London in 1919 by a Mr Shire who farmed near Taunton, and was used for threshing and timber cutting work until retired in 1954. It has since been beautifully restored.

above left: Field Marshall diesel tractors were built by Marshall, Sons & Company of Gainsborough. The Series 1 was introduced in 1945 and the Series 2, seen here, in 1947. To start it, a smouldering piece of salt-petre-impregnated paper was inserted into the cylinder head and the flywheel rotated by cranking a starting handle until ignition was achieved. Marshalls merged with John Fowler & Co. of Leeds in 1947 to become Marshall-Fowler Ltd and tractor production — latterly under the Leyland name — ceased in 1992.

top right: Fordson and Massey-Harris tractors displayed at a vintage gathering in Wiltshire.

above right: A John Deere tractor at work, harrowing a Lancashire field.

The working life of the farmer was once governed by the seasons – and the working day dictated by the changing cycle of daylight. That particular limitation ended when tractors were fitted with headlights. Harvesting now continues well into the dry summer and autumn nights. Hedgerows have progressively disappeared as ever larger machines have been brought in to work ever-larger fields.

There is, however, a cost. The impact of the loss of hedgerows on the land's ability to absorb rainwater – and the knock-on effects of flooding as global temperatures rise and periods of intense rain increase – has only recently become an issue for study and debate.

However much we complain about the rising costs of the food we eat, that is often more about the costs of packaging and distribution than it is about the cost of farming itself. Farming on an industrial scale has, in many instances, led to

left: Ploughing a field near Loch Fada on the Scottish island of Colonsay in the early 1990s.

below: 'Fergie's Harvest Happening' is an annual event near Romsey in Hampshire — whatever the weather.

lower relative prices 'at the farm gate' than our predecessors could ever have imagined.

Some would argue, with some justification, that the costs of that improved yield have been too high – the loss of the natural sympathetic relationship between man and nature, a poorer existence for the animals themselves, and an increasing and unhealthy dependence on chemicals and antibiotics, being just some of the items which might be listed on the debit side of the balance sheet.

Luckily there are events held around the country which keep the practices, the traditions and amazing machinery of early mechanical farming alive for us to enjoy.

At some, the annual farming cycle is almost compressed into a day – with everything from ploughing with horses, steam or tractors, through to harvesting by hand, by reaper and by combine harvester all on show together.

CHINA, TILES AND GLASS

IN MY TEENS IN THE LATE 1950s, a regular slot on Sunday night television was *What's my Line*, a panel game hosted by the legendary Eamonn Andrews. In the show, four celebrity panelists were invited to ask questions of each guest in order to ascertain what they did for a living. They panel started off with ten points. Whatever the question, the guest was only allowed to answer 'yes' or 'no'. If the panelists got a 'yes', they could ask another question. If they got a 'no' they lost a point, and most occupations were guessed well before all ten points had been lost.

opposite page: The inside of one of the magnificent bottle ovens at Stoke's Gladstone Pottery Museum, the last complete ceramics works of its kind in Britain — stacked with hundreds of the clay 'saggers' in which the domestic tableware was fired.

left: The tandem compound engine by Marshall, Sons & Company of Gainsborough was installed in the Gladstone Works in Stoke-on-Trent in 1901, and drove overhead driveshafts and belts to power the blungers, pug mills and slip works.

below left: Round the base of each bottle oven there were a number of access doors to the furnaces which had to be kept constantly fuelled during the long firing process — hot, dangerous, unpleasant and very unhealthy work.

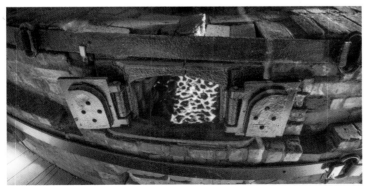

In the industry's heyday, within just a few streets of the Gladstone Pottery, there were over sixty bottle ovens. Estimates as to how many ovens there were in the five pottery towns as a whole, vary between 2000 and 4000. Fewer than four dozen of them survive, five of those within the Gladstone's yard.

opposite top left: The mould-making workshop at the Gladstone Pottery.

opposite top right: Finished chinaware ready for dispatch.

There was one, now legendary, exception who beat the panel – the 'Saggar-maker's bottom knocker'.

Saggars are the large fireclay containers used to hold pottery during firing in a kiln or bottle oven, and making them to the exacting specifications to withstand the ferocious heat of the kiln without splitting or distorting – a split would cause excess heat to reach the delicate chinaware inside – was a skilled job and needed a skilled man. He was the saggar-maker.

However, making the bases of the saggars required less precision and could therefore be left to a less skilled worker. He was the saggar-maker's bottom knocker. His job was to put a lump of clay in wooden, or later metal, frame and, as his job title suggests, knock it into a perfectly flat circular base. This was usually a role fulfilled by boys, leaving the final assembly of the saggar to the more experienced man.

The work of the saggar-maker and his bottom knocker was constantly in demand, each saggar lasting only around forty firings before it became too brittle to be safely used.

The business of manufacturing quality tableware required a wide range of skills, some demanding, others relatively mechanical. In today's highly mechanised world, most of them have now been largely consigned to history.

below: The skill of the artist is demonstrated each day in the hand-painted ceramics produced — and on sale — at Gladstone.

The atmosphere in the industry's heyday must have been pretty much un-breathable, explaining graphically why life expectancy was so short amongst those who put china on our dining tables.

Because of the inhalation of dust from clay and flint, pottery workers routinely experienced considerable damage to their lungs – those same lungs which had to breath the heavily polluted and smoke-filled air. It is, therefore, little wonder the average life expectancy in the ceramics industry just over a century ago was little more than the mid forties.

left: This view of
the skyline of the
Potteries towns,
probably taken in
the early 1920s gives
some sense of the
number of bottle
ovens then in
operation and the
polluted atmosphere
which hung daily over
the potteries towns.
As late as the 1950s
it is said that nearly
2000 of these ovens
were still in use
despite the
increasing popularity
of electric ovens and
the drive towards
cleaner air.

opposite page: There
are six surviving
bottle ovens from
Charles Pickman's
factory at la Cartuga
in Seville, five of
them in a line
running from the
remains of the
medieval abbey
church out across
the cloister.

inset: The pottery's
name and decorated
panels, displayed
over the main
gateway, are made
up of locally
produced Triana
tiles. The factory,
one of the major
employers in
the Seville area,
remained in
operation until 1982
when production
was moved to a new
facility just outside
the city.

The era of the bottle oven came to an end in most potbanks long before the Gladstone closed its doors – alternative methods of firing kilns such as gas or electricity being more efficient, more reliable and above all more predictable.

Many potteries simply demolished the ovens and replaced them with their modern successors. Now the majority of those have gone as well. The last-ever firing of a traditional coal-fired bottle oven took place over eight days in August 1978, just a few streets away from the Gladstone at the nearby Hudson and Middleton Works.

Making tableware rarely involved the traditional idea of a potter bent over a potter's wheel. Much of it was moulded or cast, using a variety of techniques, and the moulded clay was then slowly dried before its first firing.

The starting point for moulded wares was a fine malleable piece of clay which could be pressed into a plaster-of-Paris mould, while for casting, 'slip' or semi-liquid clay was used. Cast wares inevitably had seams when removed from the mould, and needed to be 'fettled' (wonderful word) to remove the rough edges before being dried and fired.

At the beginning of the twentieth century, skilled potters were paid piecework rates, the rates being based on how many full boards of clayware they produced. The board was known as a 'dozen' but depending on the size and complexity of the wares being produced, a dozen could be less than twelve or many more. Each potter had a team of semi-skilled or unskilled workers who he paid out of his own wages, so

above: An early tile press displayed in the Gladstone Museum.

opposite top left: Twelfth century tiling in the sanctuary at Byland Abbey, Yorkshire.

top right: Thirteenth century encaustic tiles at Shaftesbury Abbey, Dorset

bottom right: Late thirteenth century encaustic tiles at Cleeve Abbey, Somerset. The double-headed eagle was the motif used by Richard, Earl of Cornwall.

bottom left: An advertisement for Minton tiles c.1903.

getting as much out of each member of the team was essential. If someone carrying a 'dozen' laden with teacups dropped any of them on his way to the drying shed – known as the Greenhouse – the potter would suffer loss of earnings, and pass that loss on to his team.

Biscuit ovens were used for the first firing and after that biscuit firing, the cups, saucers, plates and other wares were glazed and decorated before being fired for a second time, this time in the 'Glost oven'.

The range of quantity of ceramics produced in eighteenth and nineteenth century Britain was considerable, and British tableware was exported all over the world.

A major exporter of fine British china in the early years of the nineteenth century was Liverpool merchant Charles Pickman who exported large quantities of Minton, Wedgwood and other high quality tableware to Spain. A series of protectionist laws passed in Spain between 1835 and 1837, however, meant that the high tariffs on imported china effectively rendered his trade uneconomic.

Pickman made a momentous decision – to relocate to Spain and develop manufacturing facilities in Seville. In 1840 he bought the former Carthusian monastery of Santa Maria de las Cuevas, changed its name to La Cartuga de Sevilla, and set about converting it into a ceramic tile factory.

Bottle ovens, a variation on the design he knew from Staffordshire, were erected on the site, and as the enterprise was something quite new for that part of Andalusia, he brought in a team of craftsmen from Stoke-on-Trent to train his local workforce – most of whom he had recruited from the handmade tile industry in nearby Triana.

He introduced staff training programmes and production-line manufacture, and by the end of the nineteenth century the factory had gained a reputation for the highest quality

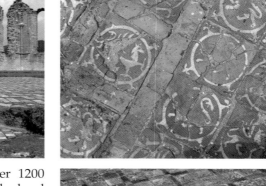

tableware and employed over 1200 people, mainly women from the local community. La Cartuga even exported Seville-made tablewares back to Britain, in a reversal of the trade Pickman had initially set up – an unlikely, but very successful, outpost of British industry.

Kiln-fired ceramics have been produced in Britain for millennia, and in addition to the thousands of exquisite items of pottery preserved in museums across the country, early examples of floor tiles can still be seen *in situ* in many medieval churches, abbeys, priories and castles.

The manufacture of ceramic tiles in Britain can trace its origins back to the second half of the tenth century,

right: The canal-side
Coalport China
factory — now the
Coalport China
Museum, one of the
constituent museums
of the Ironbridge
Gorge World Heritage
Site — still has two of
its bottle ovens

below: A decorative
tile panel, on display
in the Tile Gallery at
the Gladstone
Pottery Museum.

below right: The
ubiquitous plain
white machine-made
tile, seen here in the
pithead baths at the
Big Pit in Blaenavon,
South Wales.

when some religious communities sought to replace packed
earth or stone-covered floors with something which was both
more durable and more attractive.

Many of the early tiles were plain and small, used to create
mosaic floors, but a variety of more sophisticated manufacturing techniques evolved, introducing patterns and

colours using an ever-expanding palette of glazes. Some tiles with simple geometric designs have been excavated from Saxon sites dating back to the late tenth century.

The real popularisation of the ceramic tile in Britain began in the late thirteenth century – a century after such flooring had become popular in central Europe – and within a very few years, many monasteries had their own 'in house' tile workshops where the monks and lay brothers manufactured tiles, not just for their own use, but to fulfill commissions from other churches, abbeys and priories.

From the middle of the thirteenth century, Cleeve Abbey in Somerset had a thriving tileworks, and the results of their craftsmanship can still be seen in the large areas of surviving heraldic tiles – dating from the 1270s – which are preserved in situ in the remains of the monks' frater.

Several of the most popular medieval designs enjoyed a revival in the Victorian Gothic period of the mid nineteenth century, with the Minton works producing them in vast numbers. Many Victorian churches – and Victorian restorations of earlier churches – feature Gothic-inspired Minton tiles in their chancel floors, as do the Houses of Parliament.

below: The Red House Glass Cone in Wordsley, West Midlands, the largest and most complete of the four surviving examples of this once-common glass manufacturing structure.

Indeed nineteenth century English potteries became world-renowned for their reproductions of Gothic floor tiles, with examples surviving around the globe, including the floor of the Capitol building in Washington.

Looking externally quite similar to the ceramics industry's bottle ovens, Glass Cones were once just as common a site in glassworks across the UK from the middle years of the eighteenth century.

Now just four remain – one in Scotland at Alloa Glassworks, another at Lemington on Tyneside, a third at Catcliffe in Rotherham, and the best preserved of the four, the Red House Cone in Wordsley in the West Midlands, now a working museum operated by Dudley Council.

right: Medieval stained glass in the west window of Salisbury Cathedral. The cathedral has a team of experts who now undertake glass restoration projects for numerous other churches.

below: Glass blower Malcolm Andrews demonstrates his skills in the Red House Glass Cone.

below right: The village shop at Robert Owen's model industrial community at New Lanark. Small panes of glass – today considered to be picturesque – were a necessity imposed by the limitations of the glass-making processes of the time.

As a great deal of heat was needed for the manufacture of glass, it is not surprising that glassworks were established close to major coalfields – in Central Scotland, the North West of England, Tyneside, Yorkshire, the Midlands and the Bristol area. Those areas also had ample supplies of silica and clay – especially the sort known as 'pot-clay' which could withstand very high temperatures.

As with many industries, old technologies were swept away when new production methods came along, so the survival of any vestiges of eighteenth and nineteenth century glassworks are understandably few and historically priceless.

There are no records of how many glass cones were in operation across Britain, but the Catcliffe cone, built c.1740, is now the oldest in Europe.

Lemington once had four, all completed by 1787 of which only the largest survives.

The Red House Cone was built between 1788 and 1794, and across the road once stood the White House Cone, the site of which is now being redeveloped as a museum by the British Glass Foundation with opening planned for 2017.

The Alloa cone is the youngest of the four, completed around 1825 and is unique in having an octagonal base.

The design of the cone was vital in creating the high temperatures needed in glass-making. Air was drawn in through a series of tunnels into the heart of the furnace and then upwards into the cone. The interior temperature could be very high. But unlike pottery workers, most of whom could exit the kiln before it was fired, the glass-makers had to endure the intense heat inside the cone.

Several dozen men and children – some as young as eleven – worked within the relatively confined space inside the Red House Cone, some of them fuelling the furnaces and maintaining the temperature at around 1200°C, others keeping the crucibles filled with the basic raw materials.

With such high temperatures, the effect on the workers' lungs was considerable – yet another industry where life expectancy was shortened by working conditions which would now be unacceptable.

Glass is basically 55-70% sand (silica) to which is added lime, dolomite, soda, feldspar and potash. If lead crystal was being made – and Red House Cone was used for many years

above: A colourful display of spirits bottles at a packaging exhibition in the NEC. Until the second half of the nineteenth century most bottles were made individually by blowing the semi-molten glass into a former or mould. Today's manufacturing processes are now fully automated, with bottles and jars mass-produced in machines by one of two methods – one is known as 'Press and Blow', the other 'Blow and Blow'. Both involve the shaping of the plasticised glass inside the mould using high temperature hot air.

right: Today's glass-making demonstrations in the Red House Cone use a small gas-fired glass kiln.

middle: Looking up inside the Red House Glass Cone. The giant eighteenth century structure stands one hundred feet tall; the glass furnace in the centre would have been about 23 feet in diameter and 10 feet high. It held ten or twelve glass melting crucibles in a ring inside the furnace.

bottom: Inside the kiln, the glass is maintained at a temperature of around 1200˚C, being withdrawn and blown gently to keep the walls of the vessel being created as even as possible as the size of the object is increased.

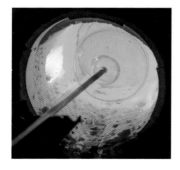

from around 1920 to make Stuart Crystal – the silica content was around 55% and 33% of the constituents had to be lead. Other crystals used a lower lead content.

As production methods evolved over the centuries it became apparent that the constituents could be combined in varying ratios, each composition imparting specific characteristics and strengths to the finished product.

Broken glass – known as 'cullett' – was also added, reducing waste and helping keep the temperature consistent.

The furnace was kept lit night and day and there are records of some furnaces burning continuously for as long as twenty-five to thirty years before their linings needed replacement.

The crucibles were filled with the basic raw materials – while, around them, the glass blowers created the bottles, glasses and other objects. One group, known as 'teasers', were responsible for fuelling and controlling the furnace. The heat was such that they were even paid a drinks bonus to assuage their thirsts.

Once shaped or moulded, it was the cooling process – known as annealing – which gave the glass its strength – cooling it too quickly left it brittle. So the finished glass was moved into a heated tunnel known as the 'Lehr' where it was allowed to cool in a slow controlled manner.

Glass produced in these cones – usually referred to as 'cylinder-blown sheet glass' – was drawn out and blown into long iron moulds to create tubes which were then cut along their lengths, reheated, flattened out and rolled into sheets – a slow and delicate process which meant that larger sheets of glass were very expensive.

Those limitations were directly responsible for the creation of windows made up of multiple small panes, in the Georgian and early Victorian eras.

above: Malcolm Andrews uses a range of simple tools to persuade the hot glass to take up the desired shape.

above left: The finished – but still very hot – glass objects were placed on trays in the annealing oven or 'Lehr' and slowly moved from the heated end to the cool end. It was important that the glass cooled in a controlled environment to avoid it cracking or becoming brittle. That process could take many hours before the glass was at room temperature. The thicker the glass, the longer it took to cool safely.

right: The Crystal Palace in Hyde Park used 300,000 sheets of rolled sheet glass made by Chance Brothers to glaze its walls and roofs. At the time, they were the largest sheets of glass ever mass-produced, each measuring 4ft x 10ins, approximately 1.25m x 25cm.

middle: The Temperate Palm House at Edinburgh's Royal Botanic Gardens was designed by Robert Matheson, who held the post of Architect for Scotland in H.M. Office of Works. It was completed in 1858 at a cost of £6000, paid for with a Government grant. At 72 feet (22m) high it is the tallest glass house in Britain, its large glass dome designed to accommodate the tallest palm trees.

right: The ornate Palm House in Liverpool's Sefton Park was completed in 1894 by Mackenzie & Moncur of Edinburgh.

The breakthrough in creating large sheets of glass at a lower unit cost was made by James Hartley in 1838. His 'Patent Rolled Plate Glass' process involved the pouring of molten glass on to a large cast-iron bed where it was rolled out by heavy iron rollers before being trimmed to size.

Other makers were experimenting along similar lines – most notably Chance Brothers of Smethwick whose glass was used to glaze Joseph Paxton's Crystal Palace which housed the 1851 Great Exhibition in Hyde Park. Just three years earlier Paxton had used large sheets of Chance glass for his 1848 hothouse at Chatsworth in Derbyshire.

Large sheets of glass revolutionised architecture – not just in the ability to create spectacular buildings such as the

below: Kibble's Palace in Glasgow's Botanic Gardens is one of the most memorable and astonishing structures in the city. John Kibble originally intended the building – enlarged from his conservatory at his house near Loch Long – to be erected in the city's Queen's Park as a concert hall and entertainment venue, but when the city refused to allow him to fill it with statues – considered by some to be immoral – he withdrew his offer and gifted the building to the Botanic Gardens. It was opened in its present location in 1874 and now houses part of the National Collection of tree ferns and other rare plant species. It was extensively restored in 2006.

above: Camberwell Green Dairy's large plate glass frontage in the mid 1860s. This ambrotype photograph of the dairy is, of course, itself taken on a sheet of glass.

opposite page left: Gateway House on the approach ramp to Manchester's Piccadilly Station, was completed in the late 1960s, its façade a striking curved structure of metal and glass.

opposite page right: Manchester's Big Wheel perfectly reflected in the float glass windows of a city-centre store.

Crystal Palace and botanical hothouses, but also in the changes which were possible on streets across the country.

Where shops had formerly had a relatively unimposing presence on the high street – with dark interiors lit through tiny windows and little in the way of light or opportunity for the proprietors to display their wares to customers – large plate glass windows introduced the whole idea of window-shopping. Now they could tempt passers-by into their premises by prominently displaying their latest wares.

Over time, the production of larger sheets of glass became easier, but plate glass required extensive and expensive grinding and polishing after casting in order to create a smooth clear surface.

Manufacturing techniques changed out of all recognition with the invention of the Float Glass process by Alastair Pilkington in the early 1950s.

Not a member of the Pilkington family but with the same surname as the company for whom he worked, his revolutionary idea was to pour molten glass on to a bath of molten tin. The glass spread out evenly over the tin creating a perfectly smooth continuous sheet of glass. It made every other process obsolete – all the grinding and polishing operations at the end of earlier production processes could be eliminated.

Float glass plants can run continuously for ten-fifteen years, creating the huge expanses of glass of various thicknesses and qualities used in everything from phone and tv screens, car windscreens and other smaller products, right up to the massive and strong sheets used to glaze the tall buildings which increasingly dominate the modern world.

When the float process was first invented, nobody knew how long the refractory bricks which lined the inside of the melting kiln, or tank, would last, being constantly subjected to such intense heat. Would they last months, or perhaps years? A sudden failure of the lining could spell disaster, requiring the production line to be shut down while the kiln was rebuilt, so staff photographers in the 1960s were required to take it in turns periodically to poke cameras into the interior of the kiln – by removing bricks at regular intervals along each side of its full length – to check for signs of cracks or deformation of the bricks.

The basic but solidly built metal-bodied Pentax cameras – no autofocus or built in exposure meters in those days – lasted two or three such explorations, the photographer's eyebrows just the one before the 1600°C heat singed them off.

Fifty years later, computers and cctv monitor the process constantly, and staff photographers are a thing of the past – not just in glass-making, but pretty much across all of manufacturing industry.

Glass can now be made with specifically engineered qualities, in thicknesses from a fraction of a milli-metre right up to heavyweight armoured materials, and with strength and flexibility which just a few years ago would have been considered impossible.

Where once it was simply used to let light in, today's glass has become an integral part of the structural rigidity of many high-rise buildings.

ALL THE FUN OF THE FAIR

INDUSTRY AND ART COME TOGETHER in a great many enterprises, and seldom has that fusion been more flamboyant than in the great fairground attractions designed, engineered and decorated in Victorian and Edwardian Britain. That they still have the same allure that they did more than a century ago is a testament both to their creators, and to the nostalgia we feel for the simpler, pre-electronic, world for which they were created.

But make no mistake, these leviathans of the entertainment world were engineering masterpieces, embodying some of the latest technologies of their day. At the heart of each, originally, was a steam engine – using exactly the same technology which pulled trains, worked farm machinery, pumped sewage and powered mills.

The Victorian and Edwardian fairground must have been a magical place, combining bright lights and thrills with leading-edge engineering, and that period magic is preserved for us to enjoy in several heritage fairgrounds and museums across the country.

While a full list is given in the Gazetteer section of this book, some notable locations are the Hollycombe Collection in Hampshire, the Scarborough Fair Collection in Yorkshire,

opposite page: The Venetian Gondola Switchback in the Thursford Collection – the last working example of its kind – was built by Savages of Kings Lynn in 1889.

below left: A gilded dragon by Britain's greatest fairground woodcarvers, Arthur Anderson & Son, c.1915-1920, is now in the Musée des Arts Forains in Paris.

below: The outer circle of horses on Carter's Jubilee Gallopers was also carved by the Andersons, c.1910.

right: Originally driven by a centre engine but now powered by electricity, the Gallopers at the Thursford Collection in Norfolk were built locally by Frederick Savage & Company at their St Nicholas Ironworks in King's Lynn in 1896. The company was one of the most highly regarded manufacturers of fairground engines and gallopers, several of which still operate.

below: 'Eileen', an 8hp Clayton & Shuttleworth portable engine built in 1926 with works number 50010, is one of the engines used to generate power for the fairground rides at the Hollycombe Steam Collection in Hampshire. The Lincoln company built its first portable engine in 1845, and its first steam-powered threshing machine just four years later. During the First World War they diversified into aircraft manufacture and built the Sopwith Camel which is credited with shooting down Baron Manfred von Richthofen, the famous 'Red Baron'.

the Thursford Collection in Norfolk, Dingles Fairground Heritage Centre in Devon and the travelling Carter's Steam Fairs which can be enjoyed at various locations around the South of England.

In Paris, several survivals of British fairground art can be seen in the wonderful Musée des Arts Forains in Les Pavillons de Bercy.

Several names stand out in the history of the steam fairground, amongst them Richard Garrett & Sons of Leiston in Suffolk, Charles Burrell & Sons of Thetford, Frederick

Savage & Company of Kings Lynn and Robert Tidman & Sons of Norwich, all in Norfolk.

While they were the designers and manufacturers of the technology which powered many of the rides, Arthur Anderson, the son of a Bristol ship carver, made a significant contribution to the art of the fairground.

The Anderson family's Bristol workshops were near the Cumberland Basin, where Brunel's SS *Great Britain* was built and where the restored ship sits today. John Anderson was renowned as one of the finest carvers of his day – making

above left: An 1889-built Savage centre engine on display at Thursford. Similar engines would have driven the merry-go-rounds at travelling fairs throughout the country.

top: Savage's nameplate on the 1889 engine.

above: A travelling fairground at Wigan in the 1970s.

left: The 1905 Savage centre engine which sits in the middle of Thursford's late Victorian Gondola Switchback is obviously not the ride's original. It is now only for show as the restored Switchback is driven by electricity.

The steam-powered Gallopers which tour as part of Carter's Steam Fair were built by Robert Tidman & Sons in Norwich c.1895. As seen today, they are something of a hybrid. The steam engine — also built by Tidmans — probably pre-dates the ride by a few years, while the horses are later. The ride had lost its original Tidman centre engine by the time the Carters bought it, but they located an identical one — or perhaps the original? — during the ride's restoration. It has since been named 'Anna' after Anna Carter. While the outer circle of horses was made by Andersons of Bristol and dates between 1900 and 1910, the inner two circles are largely modern copies. Each of the horses now carries the name of one of the family members and friends who operate the fair. The ride's 46-key Gavioli organ was built in Paris around 1900. Gallopers should never be described as carousels — that is the American name for rides which travel anti-clockwise. British-built Gallopers rotate clockwise.

left: Seven of the many steam-driven rides at the Nottingham Goose Fair, from a postcard c.1906.

below: Carters' Excelsior Steam Yachts in action in Reading. One of only two surviving sets of steam-powered yachts in Britain, this was the original fairground 'white knuckle ride'. Supplied new by Savages of Kings Lynn in 1921 for Yorkshire Showman Joseph Ling, the ride is powered by Savages' 1901 engine, No.793, known as 'Yorky', replacing No.886. which was destroyed in 1957. No.793 still carries the nameplate of Mr J. W. Waddington, its original owner.

figureheads for Bristol-built sailing ships – but by the time his son Arthur joined the business, that market was in very sharp decline.

In seeking new markets, the company turned their skills to carving fairground figures and, as this was the heyday of the travelling fair with steam-powered rides becoming ever more popular, Anderson's beautifully carved Galloper horses could soon be seen all over the country.

right: Two steam-powered rides at Oxford's St Giles Fair c.1904 — Gallopers nearest the camera, with a gondola ride beyond. The Helter-Skelter to the right was a popular entertainment both in fairgrounds and on seaside piers.

below: This view of the Wakes Week Fair at Oldham's Tommyfield Market in 1905 has Steam Yachts to the left — the tall chimney of the steam engine can be seen to the right of the swinging yacht — and what look like three sets of Gallopers and a gondola ride. While all four rides are sporting central chimneys suggesting centre steam engines, the ride nearest the camera is advertised on its fascia boards as Collins Electric Jumping Horses.

Despite fairground rides being the new focus of their business, they seem to have continued to style themselves 'Ship Carvers'.

For one of their 1903 'Heroes of the Boer War' centaur Gallopers, they carved the head of Captain Edward Smith – already considered to be a naval hero – who would, less than a decade later, become known across the world as the captain of the ill-fated RMS *Titanic*.

While Anderson's Gallopers can still be seen on numerous fairground rides, his work is considered to be of sufficient national importance that one of his figures – a carved wooden sailor used to advertise a chandler's shop – was even included in a 2014 Folk Art exhibition at Tate Britain.

The earliest mechanical fairground rides were either hand-cranked, pulled round by horses or boys with ropes, or

The pedal-powered *Velocipede* which still operates in Les Pavillons de Bercy in Paris is typical of many early mechanical rides. It is surprising just what sort of speed can be achieved when everyone is pedalling as fast as they can. This example, built in 1897, is one of only two from the period still in existence. The ride, as preserved, is a hybrid, assembled from at least two different makers. The body of the ride was originally built in Belgium by Callebaut & Decanck. The mechanics, the bicycles and rails, however, are from a British velocipede, probably of a slightly earlier vintage – hence its clockwise rotation rather than the anti-clockwise more commonly found in European and American fairs.

powered by the riders themselves, with the earliest records of such rides dating from the first half of the nineteenth century.

Pedal-powered Velocipede rides date back to the second half of the century – a fine example, assembled from Belgian and British components, can be seen at Jean-Paul Favand's wonderful 'Pavillons de Bercy' in Paris – and if you are lucky enough to visit around Christmas when the rides are all in operation, you can have a go.

The Oxford Chronicle newspaper, reporting on the 1889 St Giles Fair in the city, noted that 'the roundabouts were numerous', ranging from 'the old-fashioned ones turned with a handle to the latest improvements in steam-powered engines.'

Steam-powered rides had been introduced more than a quarter of a century earlier, with the year 1861 marking the

This British-built pedal-powered *Velocipede* was the ideal fairground ride in areas where bringing in a power source would not have been possible. This view of a travelling fairground in Dakar, Senegal, was published as a postcard probably just before the Great War.

below right: The 20-ton 8hp Burrell engine Edward VII is displayed in the Thursford Collection. Originally bought in 1905 to generate the electricity for a travelling bioscope — an early cinema show — the engine was, by 1920, powering an electric 'scenic' merry-go-round known as Thurston's Golden Dragons. One of that ride's first passengers was King Edward VII's second daughter Princess Victoria.

first outing of Thomas Bradshaw's steam roundabout at Bolton's Pot Fair.

Another example, built by local engineer Sydney George Soames at the Perseverance Works in Marsham, was first shown at Aylsham Fair in Norfolk just four years later.

Soames, an 'Engineer, Boiler Maker and General Machinist' was already established in the construction and repair of steam-driven agricultural equipment.

The *Halifax Courier* described it as 'a roundabout of huge proportions, driven by a steam engine which whirled around with such impetuosity, that the wonder is the daring riders are not shot off like cannon-ball, and driven half into the middle of next month.'

left: Built in 1895 by Charles Burrell of Thetford, Norfolk, *Emperor* — now beautifully restored and returned to steam at the Hollycombe Collection in Hampshire — is the oldest Showman's Engine in the world. It is used to generate the electricity for some of Hollycombe's fairground rides, as well as powering the lights on the Gallopers.

above: George Twigdon & Sons were the original owners of *Emperor*.

left: A merry-go-round in action at Clun Fair in Shropshire c.1905. The ride appears to be known as Custer's Grand Royal Racing Cocks, but no further information on it has yet been located.

Very similar concerns about the effects of speed on the human body had been voiced little more than a quarter of a century earlier with the introduction of steam trains travelling at what was then a terrifying 30mph.

Frederick Savage of Kings Lynn, also a manufacturer of agricultural machinery, saw the potential of such rides and developed his steam Velocipede which he also first demonstrated in the 1860s, where human pedalling was assisted by a centre steam engine.

right: Originally dating from 1885 but heavily modified in 1922, this Ruth & Sohn fairground concert organ was built in Waldkirch in the Black Forest and spent most of its working life touring German fairgrounds before being bought and brought to Britain in 1962. Rebuilt by the late Margaret Cook and Jim Hutchens, the organ is now a very popular visitor to steam fairs. Beyond it at the 2016 Great Dorset Steam Fair is 1921-built Burrell Showman's Engine *General Gough*.

middle: The Chair-o-Planes at Carter's Steam Fair rotate clockwise. The ride was probably built in Germany in the 1920s for a British owner. Beyond is the restored 1950s *Royal Windsor* Living Wagon once used by Billy Smart's Circus.

bottom: The 'Palio Game' in Jean-Paul Favand's *Musée des Arts Forains* in Paris is a modification of a British-built 'Derby Game' made by Elton Games of Liverpool in the 1960s. The new backdrop was painted in Favand's own studios, but the game itself remains essentially as designed and manufactured in Liverpool.

left: A postcard from 1903 or 1904 shows a busy day at Lincoln Fairground. A Showman's Engine — probably built by Charles Burrell & Sons in Thetford, Norfolk — with a double chimney extender in place, stands in front of the large arcade at the left of the picture, its dynamo providing power for the electric lights and whatever amusements were inside. The large globe lamps were typical of the period.

The mechanisms he devised for his Gallopers, however, are what really made his name. Although he patented his own designs, Savage was not the first to introduce such rides — credit for that must be shared amongst a number of innovators including Robert Tidman of Norwich and several other local makers.

Indeed, the system of overhead crank shafts which created the rise and fall motion of most Gallopers — including many of those built by Savages – can be attributed to Tidman. It gave a smoother ride than Savage's original design where the vertical motion was controlled by eccentric cams beneath the platform floor.

The fact that the company's success actually depended – at least to an extent – on Tidman's mechanical ingenuity didn't stop Savages from claiming in their 1902 catalogue – five years after the death of Frederick Savage himself – that they had 'patented and placed upon the market all the principal novelties that have delighted the many thousands of pleasure seekers at home and abroad'.

below: 1898-built Burrell Showman's Road Locomotive *The Masterpiece*.

73

right: The Bristol-based brothers Marshall and Bernard Hill toured their steam fairground rides extensively in the years before and after the Great War. Their steam 'Motor Switchback' ride was considered very modern in its day, having cars rather than just gondolas. The Hills were clearly very proud of this particular ride — which is thought to have debuted at Dartmouth Fair in 1908 — as it was the subject of several contemporary postcards, all with staff and visitors included.

below: The Dumfries Rood Fair was held each year — on the last Wednesday in September, a local holiday — on Whitesands by the banks of the River Nith. The fair attracted huge crowds as can be seen from this 1903 postcard. The primary function of the fair was the annual horse sale, but with the very latest in steam-driven fairground rides, for most of those attending it was just a great day out. The fair is still held each year.

In addition to his Gallopers, Savage had also patented his Switchback in 1888 – an idea which would result in some of the most popular and richly decorated rides in the fairground, showing the artistic skills of both carver and painter. With the addition of steam-generated electric lights, their rides epitomised the 'modern' fairground.

Each of Savage's splendid animals took many days to manufacture. In addition to horses, they introduced galloping peacocks, galloping ostriches and several other animals. Some of their largest rides had fifty-six horses, four-abreast, with the added thrill of lateral movement as well as vertical. Their

patented 'platform slide' allowed the horses to swing outwards as the ride gathered speed.

The Great War put a temporary stop to the manufacture of rides as the company turned its attention to aircraft construction, and after hostilities ceased it never really regained its former dominance in the fairground.

It had managed to survive a bankruptcy in 1910, but Gallopers were being overtaken in popularity by other more

above & above left:
Yates's Steam Yachts
are driven by Savage
Engine No.867 'Reg'.

below: Howard
Brothers & Sons'
Gallopers were built
in Norfolk by
Savages, in 1886.

right: David Downs' Savage steam-driven Gallopers regularly tour steam fairs. The ride is powered by Savage engine *John Bull* — see opposite — dating from 1895, although only fitted to this ride around 1940. It is believed that the engine originally fitted to the ride was a Tidman. Music is provided by an 89-key Gavioli organ

below: Showmen's Engines on show at the Great Dorset Steam Fair — nearest to the camera, Fowler's *Royal Sovereign* was built as a roller in 1931, with Pat Collins' *No.1* dating from 1920 behind it.

thrilling rides, and their last set of 3-abreast Gallopers was built in 1922. It is surprising, therefore, that a century later, restored Gallopers draw huge crowds wherever they appear, and in the twenty-first century there are even 'new-build' Gallopers on tour in Britain, their centre engines now fired by

left: The engine which drives the Howard Brothers' Gallopers, *Lady Go Lightly*, was built by Savages in 1896 and carries Works No.664.

below: *John Bull*, currently driving Downs' Gallopers, was built the year before, in 1895, and carries Works No.638, giving us an idea of the annual engine production total.

more ecologically acceptable gas rather than coal. The smell's not quite the same, though.

It would be hard to over-estimate the importance of the steam engine in the popularisation of fairgrounds. Centre engines drove most of the roundabouts; road engines were used to haul the rides from town to town as well as powering the larger ones such as steam yachts, and when electrically-powered rides started to appear, those same engines were fitted with dynamos to generate the electricity. They were so much more attractive than the large diesel generators sitting on the backs of lorries which do that job today.

COMMUNICATIONS, COMPUTERS AND CODEBREAKERS

LATE ON THE EVENING OF 23 JULY 1962 in millions of households across Britain, families waited up to see what was then considered to be little short of magic – the first television pictures broadcast live to our homes from the United States via the *Telstar 1* satellite. The first pictures ever received by the Goonhilly Satellite Earth Station in Cornwall had actually been transmitted from America on 11 July, but they were just tests.

The live feed lasted only a few minutes as the satellite quickly went out of range – this was long before the development of the complex technologies required for launching and controlling geo-stationary satellites.

The 405-line black and white analogue picture was fuzzy, and broke up periodically during the few minutes the connection lasted, but everyone who watched it knew they were witnessing history being made – that what had previously been the stuff of science fiction was becoming science fact.

The satellite had been launched just thirteen days before that historic transmission, and with hindsight, it marked the start of the modern global communications era.

opposite: The first live transatlantic tv pictures via Telstar were received by the Goonhilly Downs receiving station in Cornwall in 1962.

below: The Acoustic Mirrors at Denge near Dungeness – comprising a curved 200ft acoustic wall, a 30ft dish with the microphone post still in place, and a smaller 20ft dish, were a primitive aircraft early warning system. Developed by Dr William Sansome Tucker, a chain of them was built along the south and east coasts in the 1920s and '30s. The group at Denge is the best preserved.

above: A 1950s' telephone exchange underground at Fife's Secret Bunker.

below left: Brunel's SS *Great Eastern* had been conceived and built as the world's largest and most luxurious passenger liner, but had never managed to achieve viable passenger numbers. As a cable-laying ship, however, she excelled.

below right: Alexander Graham Bell making the world's first telephone call in America in 1876.

Interest in the event was so great that it was even celebrated in a hit record, *Telstar*, by the Tornados.

October 4th 1957 had been the date which really heralded the start of satellite communications technology. On that date the Lovell Telescope at Jodrell Bank in Cheshire tracked the world's first-ever satellite, *Sputnik 1*, into space.

That launch marked the dawn of the space age. Less than five years later, technology had evolved sufficiently for those first tv pictures to be transmitted into our homes directly from America – a remarkable rate of progress.

In just sixty years since those pivotal events, the world of communications has evolved into something our grandparents could never have imagined, but its history can be traced back hundreds of years.

2016 saw the Post Office celebrate five centuries of regular mail deliveries with a special set of stamps, but in today's world, the postal service now accounts for just a tiny percentage of the messages we send and receive – radios, televisions, computers and phones now carry the bulk of it.

The modern world of communications can be traced back to the 1830s when the electric telegraph was invented – concurrently by several inventors in Britain, Germany and America – and to the introduction of an early version of the Morse Code in 1836 allowing 'high speed' transmission of messages across telegraph wires and later by radio.

It is worth noting that the first working electric telegraph even predated the introduction of the world's first postage stamp by Rowland Hill in 1840.

The first transatlantic telegraph cable was laid as early as 1858 between Ireland and Newfoundland in Canada, and carried the first telegraph message between Britain that August. Just a month later, the cable failed.

Several further attempts to lay a new cable were carried out, most notably in 1866 by Brunel's SS *Great Eastern* – the converted former passenger liner and largest ship ever built in the nineteenth century – which not only laid a new cable, but successfully located and repaired an earlier one, thus creating two permanent links between Europe and America.

Just ten years later, Scots-born Alexander Graham Bell filed his US patent for the first electric telephone, and in the

above: On June 15 1901 the transatlantic liner RMS *Lucania* became the first Cunard vessel to be fitted with a Marconi wireless, their second being RMS *Campania* four months later. The two liners made maritime and communications history by transmitting the first ice warning between ships.

left and below left: Continuous Wave Transmitters were first used in the trenches in the Great War. These two-valve short-range radios were introduced in 1916 and greatly improved communication, but not without risk – someone had to go 'over the top' to lay out the 100ft aerial before they could be operated. The radio had a range of about 2 miles. These examples dates from 1916-1918 and are in the collection of the fascinating Museum of Communication in Burntisland, Fife.

The 14-valve AR-88 short wave radio receiver was introduced by RCA in America in early 1941 and combined high performance with reliability. The majority of units from the first production run were supplied to Britain France and Russia between 1941 and 1943. The AR-88 was used extensively at the Government Code & Cypher School at Bletchley Park as a surveillance and intercept receiver. In total RCA produced more than 25,000 of these receivers, some with their capabilities extended into the medium wave frequencies.

right: Designed in Britain by Patrick Blackett and built in America by a division of General Motors, this 1942 Bomb Sight Mechanical Computer enabled Lancaster bombers to follow a curving flight path to their target without losing aim by constantly recalculating the relative positions of aircraft and target. These mechanical computers were widely used by Bomber Command from 1942. This example is displayed in the Museum of Communication in Burntisland, Fife.

same year the Hungarian Tivadar Puskás developed the electro-mechanical switching mechanisms which made telephone exchanges possible.

The next 'big step' in the communications revolution was the invention of radio – something which had been recognised as mathematically possible as early as 1864 by Sir James Clerk Maxwell – who is sometimes referred to as 'the

Scottish Einstein'. Maxwell's most notable contribution to science was his theory of electromagnetism, recognising for the first time that electricity, magnetism, and light were all different forms of electro-magnetic radiation.

below: Shelves of assorted valves and radios of various ages displayed in the recreation of an early radio repair shop, part of the Black Country Living Museum.

Heinrich Hertz offered practical proof of Maxwell's theory when he transmitted the first radio waves – originally known as Hertzian Waves – in 1886, and radio transmission became a practical reality just eight years later thanks to Guglielmo Marconi who first demonstrated his 'wireless telegraphy' system in 1894.

A Brazilian priest successfully transmitted the human voice for the first time using radio waves in 1900 and just six years after that, on Christmas Eve 1906, the first radio broadcast was transmitted to ships off the American coast.

The ability to transmit sound rather than just dots and dashes owes much to the work of British physicist Sir John Ambrose Fleming whose 1904 invention of the thermionic vacuum tube – or 'valve' to us in Britain – paved the way for generations of electronic devices including radios, amplifiers, television, radar and many more.

By the middle of the Great War, limited range two-valve radios were available for communication in the trenches.

Thermionic valves would, in the 1940s, become key components in the development of *Colossus* at the Government Code & Cypher School at Bletchley Park – the world's first electronic computer which played such a crucial role in code-breaking during the latter stages of the Second World War.

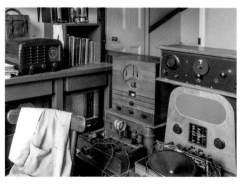

But the earliest successes at code-breaking in Bletchley Park were achieved not through the emerging computer technology – then really little more than a theoretical possibility but actively being developed – but with the help of an

right: The 3-core German *Enigma* machine with its top cover open to show the rotors. Cracking the encrypted messages sent using this machine was crucial to the Allied success in the Second World War.

below: The British *Modified Typex* or *Type X* machine used at Bletchley Park to decipher the intercepted German messages, using settings predicted by the *Bombe*. The author's aunt used one of these machines while working in 'Hut 6' in Block D at Bletchley Park from 1943 until 1945. To mimic the operation of the *Enigma*, two of the *Typex's* five cores were disengaged.

opposite page: The front face of the rebuilt Turing-Welchman *Bombe* which can be seen in operation at Bletchley Park today.

electro-mechanical machine known as the *Bombe* conceived by Alan Turing and Gordon Welchman and realised by Harold 'Doc' Keen of the British Tabulating Machine Company of Letchworth in Hertfordshire.

The *Bombe* was not a computer; it was a machine designed from scratch to perform a very specific task – to speed up the process of determining, from the 17,576 possible settings, the likely start position on the three cores of the German *Enigma* machine which had been used to encrypt the intercepted message.

But *Enigma* machines were much more complicated than that – each had a plug-board at the front, the ten connections used being rewired daily, thus increasing the number of false encryption settings which had to be eliminated if the code was to be broken to 159 million million million. You would have four million million times greater chance of winning the lottery than cracking that unaided.

To narrow the choices down, Wrens worked at the back of each machine trying out different cross-pluggings until a set-

right: The internal circuitry and mechanics of the rebuilt *Bombe*. Work on the rebuild started in 1996 and the machine was successfully operated for the first time in 2007.

below: The *Bombe Checking Machine* used to confirm the *Bombe's* suggested settings.

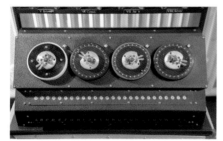

up was found which worked. The process could be often be completed in as little as fifteen minutes.

Finding all the rest of the settings was the job of the codebreakers, but the *Bombe* opened the door into what had been an impenetrable cypher.

Once the positions had been identified – and tested and confirmed on the *Checking Machine* – they were then set up on the *Modified Typex* (or 'Type X') Machines which, if the settings were correct, could then start to convert the coded messages back into their original German.

The *Bombe* was a large and complex machine for its day, and by the end of the war, more than two hundred of them were in use at Bletchley Park and its outstations, greatly speeding up the decoding operation.

Soon, however, they could not keep up with the increasing volumes of coded traffic and were ultimately superseded by devices able to unscramble much more sophisticated encryption a lot more quickly.

Most of these pioneering machines were dismantled after the war ended, keeping their workings – and even their existence – secret was of continuing national importance.

Recreating the *Bombe* which can now be seen working at Bletchley posed a formidable challenge – in the absence of official documentation, the rebuild team led by John Harper had just a few photographs, and some of the circuit diagrams released by GCHQ to go on.

Work started in 1995, and the rebuilt *Bombe* was run for the first time in 2007 – the first time one of these ground-breaking machines had been run since 1945.

The *Tunny Machine,* which was developed in 1942, was used to break the German *Sägefisch* or *FISH* code which was used for encrypted German teleprinter messages. *Tunny* used thermionic valves for the first time, and relied heavily on technology then in use in Britain's telephone exchanges.

The National Museum of Computing, also on the Bletchley Park site, has a rebuilt *Tunny* and its banks of relays will be familiar to anyone with a knowledge of how analogue telephone exchanges worked.

Just a year after *Tunny, Colossus Mk.1,* the world's first electronic computer started to unlock the secrets of the Germans' 12-core *Lorentz* machine.

below: The rebuilt Tunny machine at the National Museum of Computing.

In 2016, for the first time since the end of the war, all the mechanical and electrical equipment necessary to decode the Lorenz messages was brought together for a special event in the same building – now part of the National Museum of Computing – where it had operated seventy years earlier.

At the heart of *Colossus 1* were 1500 valves and many other 'off the shelf' components used in telephone exchanges. *Colossus Mk.II* followed very shortly afterwards, with 2500 valves.

When work started to rebuild *Colossus Mk.II*, the late Tony Sale and his team similarly had little to work from except a few photographs and some incomplete circuit diagrams.

They did, however, have the memories of the machine's original

creator, Tommy Flowers (1905-1998), the unsung hero of the computer revolution. That the team was successful in rebuilding a working example of this remarkable machine is an amazing achievement – almost as remarkable as the development of the original machine in the first place.

At the time of the rebuild, electro-mechanical telephone exchanges were being decommissioned, so there was a ready supply of components for the project – amongst them stores full of the right sort of valves.

Interestingly, rebuilding *Colossus II* actually started two years before the rebuilding of the *Bombe* with the machine being switched on for the first time in 2006.

A total of ten *Colossus Mk.II*s were built in 1944, and today's new-build stands in Block H (now the National Museum of Computing) on the site which was once occupied by *Colossus* No.9.

From those early devices grew the range of powerful computers on which we depend so heavily today – but nobody could have imagined in the 1940s the complexity and computing power of the devices we all carry round our necks, in our pockets or wear on our wrists just seventy years later.

The rebuilt *Colossus* fills a room, while the tiny chip inside the Canon 5D MkIII camera used to take the pictures of it on these pages has several hundred thousand times its computing power.

opposite page: The National Museum of Computing's Colossus Mk.II – a working replica of the most complex machine built during World War II.

above left: A working replica of 'Baby' – the world's first stored-programme computer – is displayed in the Museum of Science & Industry in Manchester. The original was built in 1948 at the city's University.

above: This mid-1960s' hard disk, 3 feet in diameter – displayed at the National Museum of Computing – could store just 8mb of data, 4mb on each side. A modern 3Tb portable hard drive, at only 2.5 inches (64mm) in diameter, has 375,000 times the capacity.

ROADS AND BRIDGES

THE POET LAUREATE ROBERT SOUTHEY once described his friend Thomas Telford, the Eskdale shepherd's son who became one of Britain's finest engineers, as the 'Colossus of Roads' – so important was Telford's contribution to developing the nation's transport infrastructure.

On a plaque on the bridge which crosses the River Moriston at Invermoriston on the north shore of Loch Ness, can be read the claim that this bridge was 'one of nearly a thousand built by Telford between 1803 and 1819' to improve the nation's transport system.

'Telford's is a happy life,' wrote Southey in his account of a journey the two men made together through Scotland in 1819, 'everywhere making roads, building bridges and erecting harbours – works of sure, solid, permanent utility'.

On their Scottish journey they visited many of Telford's current projects, returning south along one of his greatest achievements – the Caledonian Canal.

At the time, Telford was working for the Roads Commissioners who sought to improve the transport infrastructure across the country to cater for the growing numbers of vehicles using the pitted and pot-holed roads which existed at the beginning of the nineteenth century.

Potholes, it would seem, are a centuries-old curse and not a just blight on the present-day road user.

opposite page: The most famous of London's bridges, Tower Bridge, was opened by the Prince of Wales in 1894. The Tower Bridge Exhibition now allows visitors to explore this iconic structure and the Newcastle-built Victorian steam engines which once powered it.

below left: The Conway Suspension Bridge, one of the first suspension road bridges in the world, was designed by Thomas Telford to carry the main road from Chester to Bangor. It was opened to traffic in 1826. It spanned 99.7m (327ft), a massive achievement in its day.

above: Telford also designed the castellated tollhouse at the eastern end of the bridge – seen here through the bridge's wrought-iron suspension chains.

91

top: The Palladian Bridge over the River Nadder at Wilton House, was designed by the 9th Earl of Pembroke and Roger Morris, 1737-1739.

middle: Bath's eighteenth century Pulteney Bridge was designed by Robert Adam.

above: Lincoln's High Bridge, albeit much modified, can trace its origins back to the twelfth century.

Southey related a story of some travellers coming south, who were shocked when their horses stumbled and the coach jolted violently. 'What's the matter?' one of them asked the driver, who replied 'Perthshire – we're in Perthshire, Sir' as if that statement needed no further explanation.

But, Southey also noted, where new roads had been built to Telford's specification, there were others who were equally unhappy – 'The blacksmith at Fort Augustus complains that in consequence of the improvement, his business in repairing carriages is lessened to the amount of seven pound a year, and the blacksmith at Inverary [sic] computes his yearly loss at fifteen.'

In a career spanning more than sixty years, Telford's vision changed the face of Britain. As well supervising the construction of countless miles of roads, docks and harbours, he designed and oversaw the construction of some of the most imposing bridges of his day, hundreds of miles of canals, and a host of little churches.

What marks Telford's bridges out is their originality of design. He did not simply replicate the same bridge all over Britain – he created a rich variety of designs, each immediately in sympathy with its surroundings, and all today listed as architecturally important.

Amongst his many bridges, the solidly built Tongland Bridge over the River Dee in Dumfries and Galloway, the elegant Craigellachie Bridge over the Spey in the north east of Scotland, the suspension bridge at Conwy and the Waterloo Bridge at Betws-y-Coed, both crossing the River Conwy are testaments to that originality.

TABLE of TOLLS.

above: The 19-arch Leaderfoot railway viaduct near Melrose in the Scottish Borders, described as 'immense' by Queen Victoria when she saw it in 1865, was designed by Charles Jopp and Edinburgh civil engineers Wylie & Peddie.

left: The world's first Iron Bridge, built by Abraham Darby III between 1778 and 1779, and opened in 1781, crosses the Severn in Ironbridge.

inset: The Table of Tolls for the Iron Bridge.

bottom: The legend 'This arch was constructed in the year Waterloo was fought' runs across the span of Thomas Telford's 1815 Waterloo Bridge at Betws-y-Coed.

right: 'We came upon Craig-Elachie Bridge, one of Telford's works,' wrote Southey, 'and a noble work it is. The whole cost of the bridge and approaches on each side was £8,200.' The cast-iron bridge near Aberlour in Moray, one of the finest and most beautiful in Britain, has a span of 45.7m (150ft). It was constructed between 1812 and 1814. Despite there being several well-established iron foundries in Scotland, much closer to the construction site, the ironwork was cast at Cefn Mawr near Ruabon in Denbighshire at the Plas Kynaston iron foundry by Telford's favourite iron-founder, William Hazledine, who had already cast the ironwork for several of his bridges. It was then transported by canal, ship and horse-drawn trailers to Speyside.

right: Looking rather neglected, Telford's unique Bannockburn Bridge, bridging a deep cutting through which the Bannock Burn flows, is almost obscured from view.

Most unusual, perhaps, is that which links Seil Island to the Scottish Mainland near Oban. Until the completion of the Skye Bridge in 1995, this tiny span, basking in the acquired name of the 'Atlantic Bridge', could claim to be the only bridge to span the Atlantic Ocean.

Bridges are as old as civilisation itself, essential whenever a river or a gorge needed to be crossed. Bridges brought communities together, and by medieval times, bridges were even structures on which people lived and worked.

Early paintings of London Bridge are well-known, showing buildings lining both sides, and there were once numerous others. Today only two remain – Lincoln's High

Bridge dating originally from the twelfth century, and Bath's Pulteney Bridge, designed by Robert Adam in the Palladian style and completed by 1774. It connected the old city with the new Georgian town of Bathwick across the River Avon.

While Lincoln's bridge has buildings along one side only, Pulteney Bridge is unique in having shops built across its full span on both sides. While Palladian in design, Pulteney Bridge is very much in the medieval tradition.

Just four years later work started on the world's first arched bridge made of iron – bringing with it a hint of the industrial future, but actually assembled with dovetailed joints in precisely the same way as it would have been had the spans been made out of wood.

With the opening of the canals, and the railways, bridge-building in Britain increased significantly as the number of obstacles to be crossed doubled and then doubled again, and those on the expanding railway network were required to span ever-wider crossings and that, together with the increasing weight of the vehicles using those bridges required

below left: Telford designed his Tongland Bridge in Dumfries & Galloway to echo the architecture of a Scottish castle.

bottom left: The Atlantic Bridge links Seil Island off the west coast with the Scottish mainland, hence its nickname.

below: An old road sign seen near the Wookey Hole Caves in Somerset.

right: Brunel's single-track railway bridge over the River Tamar at Saltash, under construction in 1859.

below: When the collapsed remains of Thomas Bouch's Tay Bridge were recovered from the bed of the estuary, the locomotive and carriages were still contained within the metal bridge frame-work. The North British Railway's 4-4-0 locomotive No.224 was actually recovered, repaired at Cowlairs in Glasgow and returned to service. It was nicknamed 'The Diver' by crews who were never happy to be assigned to it. Despite remaining in service until 1919, the locomotive only ever crossed the replacement Tay Bridge once. Ironically, that was on the night of 28 December 1908, exactly twenty-nine years after it had plunged into the river. This postcard was published as part of a series in Dundee in 1902, demonstrating there was still considerable interest twenty-three years after the disaster.

the development of a whole new range of materials and engineering skills. An understandable caution, as the required length of bridges increased, meant many were actually over-engineered.

Amongst those new engineering solutions was the use of wrought iron. George Stephenson used wrought iron for his High Level Bridge over the Tyne which was opened in 1849. Stephenson's wrought-iron box-section Britannia Bridge over the Menai Straits opened in the following year. It was largely destroyed by fire in 1970 and the rebuilt bridge, while still listed as a Grade II* monument, shows little of Stephenson's work.

Isambard Kingdom Brunel watched the construction of the Menai bridge and was especially interested in the construction method, whereby the box sections were built on land, floated out and then raised between the towers. He used the same technique for his beautiful Royal Albert Bridge over the River Tamar at Saltash which was opened in 1859 shortly before his untimely death.

One notorious exception to the successful use of iron was Thomas Bouch's railway bridge over the River Tay in Scotland, completed in 1878. The bridge was the longest of its type yet built, at almost 2 miles in length and the distance between the piers – 75 metres – was twice as long as had ever been constructed before using brick and cast iron. The bridge had been intended to have a 40mph speed limit but this was reduced to 25mph by safety inspectors before it opened to traffic in July 1878. Just nineteen months later, it collapsed in a gale on the night of 28 December 1879, taking a train and its passengers – estimated at seventy-five but never confirmed – down into the icy waters of the river.

Less than eight years later, the New Tay Viaduct as the replacement bridge was originally known, designed by William Henry Barlow and built by William Arrol, opened to traffic and continues in use today.

Long before the collapse, Thomas Bouch had already been chosen as the engineer to build the proposed railway bridge across the River Forth, but he was replaced in early 1881 by Benjamin Baker and John Fowler as designers and William Arrol as builder.

below: The novel design of Edinburgh's Leamington Lift Bridge on the Union Canal enabled the roadway to be raised vertically to allow canal craft to pass beneath.

The unique cantilever design of the iconic Forth Bridge – one of the most recognisable bridges in the world – was engineered to be several times stronger than was actually needed, a reasonable precaution given the height above the river the spans were required to be. Access to the naval dockyards at Rosyth was needed at all times and the Admiralty is said to have demanded a clearance of 45 metres above high water.

Listing as a UNESCO World Heritage Site in 2015 came at a time when there are great plans ahead for the 127 year old bridge –

Scotland's Pride—The Great Forth Bridge and the Highland Kilt.
Copyright 1900 by Underwood & Underwood.

opposite: The cantilevered Forth Railway Bridge, one of Scotland's most iconic structures.

inset: Victorian photographers clamoured to take and market pictures of the Forth Bridge for tourists. This American stereo-scopic (3D) view of the bridge was taken in 1896 and remained on sale until the outbreak of the Great War.

left: The cable-stayed Queensferry Crossing nearing completion over the Forth in June 2016.

below: The AA started putting up road signs as early as 1906. Both the Myreton Motor Museum in East Lothian and the Cotswold Motor Museum have fine collections of enamel signage.

foremost amongst them being the creation of a new visitor centre under the north tower at North Queensferry, and a breathtaking 'visitor experience' which would include views of the landscape of the Lothians and Fife and as far north as Ben Lomond from the highest point on top of one of Britain's most remarkable engineering achievements.

That is something only seen by the bridge's builders in the 1880s, and the generations of engineers and painters who have kept it in operational condition ever since.

While the bridge is still an essential part of the East Coast Main Line it is, except at peak times when there are around five trains an hour in each direction, quite lightly used.

Might there even be some limited potential for a steam-hauled heritage service between North Queensferry and Dalmeny, or even on

EDINBURGH 17
HADDINGTON
DUNBAR 11
BERWICK 41
ERECTED BY THE
A.A.& M.U.

right: The Grade II*-listed, 61 metre span, Bank Quay Transporter Bridge in Warrington was built in 1915, one of three such structures to cross the River Mersey. Last used in 1964, its condition gives cause for concern. The gondola was cable-hauled from winding gear at the right hand end of the superstructure.

below: The Grand Opening Day at the Runcorn-Widnes Bridge in May 1905.

the 11 mile route between Edinburgh Waverley and North Queensferry to give visitors a truly memorable experience on their journey to the planned Forth Bridge Experience?

By the time the visitor centre opens, those views from the top will take in not only the 1964 Forth Road Bridge, but also the 2017 three-tower cable-stayed Queensferry Crossing.

However, for many river and canal crossings, where clearance was an issue in the nineteenth

right: Work underway on the Runcorn-Widnes Transporter Bridge in 1903. The towers stood 55 metres tall, and the gondola could carry three hundred people 25 metres above the River Mersey and the Manchester Ship Canal — a crossing of 300 metres. The bridge was demolished in 1961.

left: Since the opening of a new road bridge in 2005, traffic on the 1906 Newport Transporter Bridge over the River Usk has dropped considerably. The towers stand over 73 metres high, and the bridge span is just short of 200 metres.

below: Seen here from the entrance to St Katherine's Dock, London's Tower Bridge is one of the world's most iconic bridges.

century to allow the passage of tall-masted sailing vessels, a fixed bridge was not the answer. Amongst the alternatives were 'lift bridges' which could be physically raised when boats needed to pass beneath – and there were some ingenious ways of doing that – swing bridges which moved out of the way to allow traffic to sail past, and transporter bridges where passengers and vehicles were carried across rivers in gondolas

left: The Widnes-Runcorn Bridge was opened in 1961 and replaced the transporter bridge which had been the only means of getting vehicles across the Mersey since it opened in 1905. It was widened between 1975 and 1977 when it was renamed the Silver Jubilee Bridge.

suspended by cables from a wheeled platform running under the bridge's overhead stiffening beam.

Just two of the five built in Britain are still in operation today, one in Middlesbrough and the other in Newport, South Wales. A third, which links two chemical plants across the Mersey at Warrington, has not been used for almost fifty years and is now listed on the 'at risk' register of historic buildings.

The Newport Bridge – the longest of the remaining three – was designed by the Frenchman Ferdinand Arnodin who built 7 of the world total of 21. The Warrington Bridge was built by Sir William Arrol & Co. of Dalmarnock, the Runcorn-Widnes Bridge by the Arrol Bridge & Roof Co. of Springburn, Glasgow, and the Tees Bridge by Sir William Arrol and the Cleveland Bridge & Engineering Company.

By far the most famous of Britain's lift bridges is undoubtedly Tower Bridge in London, initially designed by Sir Horace Jones and given its baronial appearance by his assistant and successor George Daniel Stevenson.

Originally estimated at around £750,000, the final bill was just short of £1,200,000, so cost overruns on major infrastructure projects are not just a modern phenomenon.

Many features of the bridge were technically innovative posing considerable engineering challenges, not least of which were the huge weights involved.

Construction started in 1887, took seven years, employed over four hundred workmen, and drew crowds of visitors as work progressed. The bridge was finally opened by the Prince and Princess of Wales on 30 June 1894, allowing vessels of up to 10,000 tons to pass between the towers.

Beneath the granite-cladding of the towers which we see today is a complex steel-framed structure standing on huge concrete piers each weighing 70,000 tons. That weight was required to support the bridge itself and deal with the stresses as the counter-balanced bascules raised and lowered the roadway. At the time the piers were built, they were the largest and heaviest in the world.

As with many other contemporary projects, the steel was supplied by Sir William Arrol from his Dalmarnock Foundry in Glasgow's Dunn Street.

Mechanically, at the heart of the bridge were two massive horizontal twin-tandem compound stationary steam engines,

top: One of the four accumulators which were used to store water under pressure for the hydraulic bascule engines.

middle: One of the 1894 hydraulic bascule engines on display in the engine room.

above: Hotchkiss Circulators removed mud, air and oil from inside the steam boilers.

opposite: Tower Bridge open to allow PS *Waverley* to pass.

inset: One of the two steam engines which formerly powered the bridge lift, now beautifully restored and turned by electricity.

Isambard Kingdom Brunel was only twenty-four years old when he won a competition to design a bridge across the Avon gorge near Bristol — at the time it would have been the highest and longest suspension bridge in the world. The bridge spans 214m (710ft) and the road deck crosses the gorge 75m (245ft) above the Avon's high water level. Financial problems with the bridge's backers caused the project to be abandoned part way through construction. It was not finally completed until after Brunel's death. Entirely maintained by its tolls since it opened in 1864 — an average of 8000 cars a day pass over it — the bridge was so well built that more than 90% of the original wrought ironwork is still in place today. In contrast, modern steel cable bridges — including the Forth Road Bridge, opposite — start to develop problems after fifty years.

THIS BRIDGE
WAS DESIGNED IN 1830 BY
ISAMBARD KINGDOM BRUNEL
(1806-1859)
CONSTRUCTION BEGAN IN 1836 BUT WAS
INTERRUPTED IN 1843 THROUGH LACK OF
FUNDS. IT WAS NOT UNTIL 1864 FIVE YEARS
AFTER BRUNEL'S DEATH THAT THE BRIDGE
WAS COMPLETED AS A MONUMENT TO
HIS FAME, THE CHAINS USED BEING THOSE
FROM THE HUNGERFORD BRIDGE DESIGNED
AND ERECTED BY HIM IN 1843.

built by Sir William Armstrong, Mitchell & Company's Elswick Works in Newcastle, which pumped water under 750psi pressure into four huge vertical accumulators.

The original lifting mechanisms were powered by that pressurised water through eight three-cylinder single-acting hydraulic 'driving engines', but oil under pressure powered by electro-hydraulic motors has been used since the engines were retired in 1974.

The steam engines, still in their vast barrel-vaulted engine rooms beneath the roadway on the south side of the river, were restored and opened to the public in 1982. One of the original driving engines, no longer in situ, is displayed in the engine house.

Traffic on the river has declined hugely in recent years, and the guidebook estimates that the bridge is still opened about one hundred times each year. On the day we visited in October 2015 however, it opened eight times in less than four hours.

Remarkably, in these days when road transport dominates our lives and everything else gives way to it, Tower Bridge, and railway level crossings, are some of the few remaining places where it does not call the tune – shipping still takes precedence; cars must wait.

above: The 1964 Forth Road Bridge was built a century after Brunel's Clifton Bridge by a consortium of Sir William Arrol & Company, the Cleveland Bridge & Engineering Company and Dorman Long. When opened, it was the longest suspension bridge in Europe, with a central span of 1006m (3300ft), almost five times the span of Brunel's bridge. The newly opened Queensferry Crossing alongside it will take away most of its heavy traffic.

left: Three transport arteries in a single photograph – the Leeds to Liverpool Canal was completed in 1816. The Southport to Manchester Railway crossing over it in the distance opened in 1855 while the M6 Gathurst Viaduct was completed in 1963.

right: A Glasgow-built 1902 Albion A1 'Dog-cart' standing on the 'Time Road' at the British Motor Museum in Gaydon, Warwickshire. In this innovative display around the perimeter of the museum's main hall, period vehicles are presented standing on the types of road surfaces which prevailed at the time they were built. The Albion Motor Car Company of Scotstoun, Glasgow, sold their first vehicle in 1900, and sold sixty cars in their first two years, but by 1915 they had moved exclusively into the growing market for commercial vehicles.

Roads have long eclipsed the railways, canals and rivers as the country's major transport arteries, but even well into the nineteenth century their development was patchy. A traveller did not have to go very far from the major centres to find himself travelling on little better than dirt tracks.

Reading some early accounts of life in Britain reveals some surprising anomalies. While Thomas Telford was busy improving roads and designing or building his thousand bridges, some of the more remote parts of Britain were still unconnected by even the most rudimentary roads.

Osgood Mackenzie, in his book *A Hundred Years in the Highlands,* quoted from his uncle's diaries written in the opening years of the nineteenth century that 'there being no need for wheels in a roadless country in my young days, we had only sledges in place of wheeled carts, all made by our grieve.'

These horse-drawn sledge carts were used 'for moving peats, and nearly every kind of crop… …fish up from the shore and lime and manure… …the sledges could slide where wheeled carts could not venture, and carried corn and hay, etc., famously.'

The Gairloch area of north-western Scotland in which he lived would not get its first proper road until the 1840s, partly paid for by Mackenzie's wealthy mother.

Where there were well-laid roads, they had mostly been built by Telford who had started preparing good road surfaces using crushed stone in 1801. His methods were refined by the Scots engineer John Loudon Macadam who realised that Telford's foundations of packed rock were unnecessary and that smaller stone tightly impacted and slightly cambered from the centre were both more durable and better at dispersing water.

Macadam also discovered that the size of the stones on the surface had a critical relationship with the four inch wide wheels on early nineteenth century wagons, and it was to that form of road construction that the term 'Macadamed' was applied. Although we often make the link between 'tarmac' and Macadam, he had nothing to do with that development.

When more vehicles started using the roads – steam and petrol lorries and cars adding to the existing horse-drawn traffic – dust from the surface became more of a problem, and it was a Swiss doctor, Ernest Guglielminetti who came up with the idea in 1902 of a 'tar-bound macadamed' road, spraying the stone surface with coal tar from a local gasworks. 'Tarmac', however, is a completely different material – a product patented by the American Edgar Hooley in 1903 as 'Tarmacadam', the road surface itself being a mixture of slag from foundries and coal mines, mixed with coal tar. Modern roads are usually made of asphalt over a tightly compressed foundation of hardcore.

Road bridges, once hand-built of stone or brick, are now concrete and steel, engineered to carry the heavy weight of today's traffic, while pedestrian bridges are made of lighter materials. That has enabled a new generation of innovative lift bridges to be developed – such as Gateshead's tilting Millennium Bridge and the Salford Quays Millennium Bridge – quicker to construct, lighter and therefore easier to raise and lower simply using mains electricity.

below: A modern take on the lift bridge, the Salford Quays Millennium Bridge gives pedestrian access across the Manchester Ship Canal at the entrance to the former Manchester Docks, and links MediaCityUK with the Lowry Arts Centre. Designed by Carlos Fernandez Casado, it was completed in 2000 and, when necessary, the walkway can be raised 18 metres to allow vessels access to the redeveloped docks area. The lifting mechanism was engineered by Rotterdam-based M. G. Bennett Associates, who also designed Glasgow's Millennium Bridge and developed the tilting mechanism for the Gateshead Millennium Bridge.

ROAD TRANSPORT

CRAWLING ALONG IN A CAR behind a horse-drawn brewer's dray can be frustrating when in a hurry, but it is also a reminder of a fast-disappearing aspect of town life.

A century and a half ago, before the advent of steam vehicles and long before the motor car, the pace of the horse dictated the maximum speed at which anyone could travel on the road – and indeed, for centuries, the needs of the horse and cart, coach or carriage, dictated the very nature and construction of roads themselves.

The end of the nineteenth century and the early years of the twentieth century marked the transition from horse-drawn to motor vehicles, and buses were a very public measure of that change. Motor buses could carry many more passengers than their two-horse counterparts, and the novelty of travelling on them immediately caught the public imagination.

London's buses featured in several superbly produced series of postcards, with cards of horse-drawn vehicles available from the earliest years of the twentieth century.

opposite page: Tom and Monty (both now retired), two of the magnificent horses which pull the drays for Wadworth's Brewery in Devizes, Wiltshire, delivering beer to local pubs and hotels.

above: Many early paved roads were designed to smooth the passage of carts, the two lines of flagstones offering a slightly smoother journey than over cobbles. This early eighteenth century roadway is a relatively rare survival.

left: A sixth plate ambrotype photograph from the 1860s shows a small charabanc about to set off on a trip to the country. A vehicle like this would have been pulled by a pair of light horses.

above: A London General horse-drawn omnibus bound for London Bridge. By the time this postcard was marketed in 1904, the days of the horse-drawn bus were drawing to a close. Just a few weeks after this card was posted in February 1905, London's first motor bus appeared.

above right: The crew of the London Motor Bus Company Limited's brand new Arrow bus pose for a photographer c.1907. The advertisements which would have covered the sides of the upper deck had not yet been added. This service ran from Fulham to Liverpool Street via Waltham Green, South Kensington, Sloane Square, Hyde Park Corner, Piccadilly, Charing Cross, Strand, and Bank.

With an already established market, it is hardly surprising that bus companies used the postcard to promote their new motor buses. New vehicles, resplendent in their fresh coats of paint, and often before any advertising placards were affixed to their upper decks, were photographed with their immaculately turned out crews posing alongside them – and often with small crowds of onlookers keen both to admire them, and get themselves on to postcards!

Charles Dickens Jnr – son of the eminent novelist – devoted several pages of his 1888 *Unconventional Guide to London* to detailing omnibus services and fares, writing:

The omnibus service of London is chiefly in the hands of the London General Omnibus Company (Limited), whose carriages traverse the leading thoroughfares in every direction at regular intervals from early morning to midnight. Besides the company there are also on the principle routes one or two large private proprietors, and a considerable number of smaller owners, who run their vehicles more or less at discretion, as well as lines between the great railway stations...

...The London General Omnibus Company has lately met with fresh competition in the London Road Car Company (Limited), which has offices at 9, Grosvenor-rd, Westminster, and at the present time has convenient vehicles running on the following five lines: Victoria Stn., viâ Charing +, Fleet-st, and Bank, to Broad-st Stn., every 8 min. Hammersmith-broadway, viâ Piccadilly, Strand, etc., to Liverpool-st and London-

left: A busy day on Briggate in Leeds c.1875. The Leeds Tramways Company opened its first route on 16 September 1871 from Boar Lane to Oak Inn, Headingley, later extending the system to around 14 miles in total. All the trams were horse-drawn for the first decade, with the first trials of steam traction taking place in 1882. The company operated a mixture of horse-drawn and steam-hauled services until taken over by the City Corporation in 1893. The system was electrified in 1901 and closed in 1959.

br. Waltham-gn, viâ Fulham-rd and Piccadilly to London-br. Waltham-gn, viâ King's-rd Sloane-sq, Victoria, and Strand to Liverpool-st.

Dickens Jnr devoted more than ten pages to the London General's bus timetable, and judging by the number of routes and the frequency of the services they operated, the bus companies between them must have had several thousand horses.

A colour coding for each route had come into being as early as the 1880s, so Dickens listed the vehicle colours and styling, as well as details of the frequency and the fares on each of the one hundred and seventy-five services listed.

below; This S-Type London General Bus No.S742 was built for the company by the Associated Equipment Company — AEC — and entered service in 1923. It was one of 928 to be built by AEC and one of the last to be withdrawn from service in 1933. It is seen here on the 'Time Road' at the British Motor Museum in Gaydon, Warwickshire. Comparing this vehicle with the Arrow bus from sixteen years earlier — on the opposite page — the basic design of motor buses had changed very little between 1907 and 1923.

right: A 1927 Yorkshire Steam Wagon, seen at the 'Yesterday's Farming' show at Illminster, Somerset.

below: Standing in the rain on a damp and grey Sunday Steaming Day at Hereford Waterworks Museum, a rebuilt 1920 Foden Steam Wagon, with works No.10320, simmers quietly next to a vintage MG sports car. The Isle of Man Highway Board was the Foden's first owner, but it was originally supplied as a tipper. In its restored form, it is a flatbed. The Foden Steam Wagon Company was based at Sandbach in Cheshire, having been established as early as 1856. The Foden name continued to be used on trucks and buses until dropped by the current American owners in 2006.

bottom: Members of the Thornycroft workforce pose for the camera on the flatbed of a six-wheeled articulated steam lorry in 1897. The vehicle, was driven by a compound steam engine using a boiler from a marine launch and weighed over 4 tons. It could carry a five ton load at 5mph.

far left: The only surviving Glasgow-built Sentinel Steam Waggon is a 4 ton Standard made at the Polmadie Works in 1914 and sold new to Alexander Runcie of Inverurie.

left: The Sentinel company moved from Glasgow to Shrewsbury in 1916. This maker's plate comes from a 6 ton Waggon with Works No.1286, built in the first year in the new factory.

below: A rare steam tricycle, the 'Craigievar Express' was built by Andrew Lawson of Craigievar in 1895. In 1897 it took part in Queen Victoria's Diamond Jubilee parade in Aberdeen.

Motor buses started to appear on British streets in 1905 when London General ordered its first fifty vehicles. Some were made by De Dion Bouton, others by Sidney Straker & Squire Ltd., and by 1911 the last of the horse-drawn vehicles had been withdrawn. The second generation of motor buses, built by London General to their own standard design, first appeared early in 1910. The early motorised years were, however, marked by numerous accidents as driver training was woefully inadequate. Just because a man could control two horses, it did not necessarily follow that he could control a motor vehicle.

The advent of the motor bus also saw a step backwards in terms of route identification in London – by 1911 colour-coding of vehicles according to their route had been abandoned, and all the company's new motor buses were painted red, a tradition which endures to this day.

The first steam omnibuses were introduced by one Goldsworthy Gurney who, in 1827, was the first to build a self-propelled coach carrying fare-paying passengers.

right: The cab interior of the only surviving example of a Foden Speed-12 six-wheeled steam wagon. This immaculately restored example is a 1931 model, the year the vehicle was introduced. This vehicle, and its stablemate the Speed-6, were Foden's last production steamers.

below: Stoking the Foden Speed-12 at the 2016 Great Dorset Steam Fair.

In 1831 Charles Dance operated a steam coach service between Gloucester and Cheltenham, four times a day, at an average speed of 12mph. Another pioneer was Walter Hancock of Streatham. His first steam omnibus, an experimental ten-seater, known as the *Infant*, was completed in 1829. In 1833 Hancock built his *Enterprise* for the London and Paddington Steam Omnibus Company, a larger vehicle with a capacity of fourteen passengers, which started operating between Paddington and London Wall. *Enterprise*

required a three-man crew, one at the front and two at the rear, and could reach 20mph.

The passengers sat facing each other along the length of the machine – actually sitting on top of the two large water tanks which fed the boiler.

Hancock eventually built ten of these vehicles, giving one of them the unfortunate name of *Autopsy*. A 2002-built working replica of *Enterprise* can occasionally be seen at steam fairs and transport museums around the country.

Perhaps surprisingly, a few new steam buses were still being built more than eighty years after Hancock and Gurney's pioneering achievements – one vehicle was constructed by The Yorkshire Steam Wagon Company in 1917 for Grimsby Provincial Tramways.

above: The interior of the cab of a 1929 Foden Steam Wagon in the Thursford Collection, showing the driver controls. By the time this vehicle rolled off the production line, the days of steam traction on the roads were almost over, with petrol and diesel-engined vehicles gaining market share.

Both the London Transport Museum in Covent Garden and the London Bus Museum at Cobham Hall have large collections of buses, telling the story of public transport in the capital from 1829 to the present day.

Other towns eschewed the steam bus, preferring steam tramways with many tram locomotives in service from the 1870s until around 1900. Amongst the manufacturers were well-known names including Aveling & Porter, Charles Burrell, Manning Wardle, and Dick, Kerr & Company.

left: A steam tram engine by Thomas Green & Sons of Smithfield Foundry, Leeds, in service on the Accrington & Haslingden Tramway c.1906. Steam power was used until 1907.

top: This unusual postcard was one of several 'requiems' marking the passing of Birmingham's steam trams which were produced in 1907. The fleet had comprised 14 Kitson steam engines and 13 tramcars built by the Falcon Engine & Car Works in Loughborough. The company also made steam tram engines, but clearly Birmingham had preferred the Leeds-built Kitsons.

In Remembrance of

THE BIRMINGHAM & DISTRICT OLD STEAM TRAMS

WHICH STARTED SERVICE NOVEMBER 25th, 1884.

PASSING AWAY OWING TO AN ELECTRIC SHOCK JANUARY 1st, 1907.

"Let not ambition mock their useful toils, Their homely joys and destiny obscure."

Photo by]

[P. King.

right: The Wolverton & Stony Stratford Tramway was the last in Britain to abandon steam, even adding a Bagnall locomotive as late as 1922. In addition to the Bagnall, the original three engines from 1886 were an 0-4-0 built by Hughes of Loughborough — which later became the Falcon Engine & Car Works — another from Thomas Green, and this German-built 0-4-0 from Krauss & Co. of Munich.

right: Photographer William Hooper was on hand to record the scene when tramcar No.11 — brand new and on only its second day in service — was derailed at points on Victoria Road in Swindon on 1 June 1906, resulting in the death of five of the passengers.

THE STEAM TRAM WOLVERTON.

TRAM CAR DISASTER SWINDON. 1.6.06. HOOPER

The most prolific manufacturers were Kitson & Co. of Leeds, Beyer Peacock of Manchester and Walter Wilkinson of Pemberton near Wigan. Surviving examples include a 3ft gauge Kitson engine in Hull's Streetlife Museum – originally built for use on the Portstewart Tramway in Northern Ireland – and two Beyer-Peacock engines, both in the National Tramways Museum at Crich, Derbyshire.

One of those had been shipped to Australia for evaluation by the New South Wales Government Tramways in 1885 while the other, built for Manchester, Bury, Rochdale and Oldham Tramways, is currently undergoing restoration.

The NSW Government decided against using Beyer-Peacock engines in their fleet – preferring instead American-built Baldwins – and the engine was returned to Manchester where it was used as Works Shunter No.2 in the yard of the company's Gorton factory until 1959.

In total the Beyer-Peacock company manufactured around eighty tram engines, many of them incorporating patent gearing mechanisms licensed from Wilkinsons of Wigan.

above left: Tramcar No.49 was built by the United Electric Car Company for Wolverhampton Tramways in 1909 with an enclosed upper deck, but is open-topped in its restored form. It is seen here in the tram-shed at the Black Country Living Museum in Dudley, West Midlands.

above: Horse-drawn tramcar No.23 which was built for Wolverhampton Tramways at the Falcon Works in Loughborough in 1892 sits alongside No.49. No.23 was withdrawn in 1902 when the network was electrified.

right: A collection of cars displayed at Watts Yard Motor House & Repair Shop, 53 and 86 Sinclair Street Helensburgh in 1904. Mr Watts, *on the right*, had the photograph printed as a tinted postcard which he then mailed to all his customers in February 1905 soliciting business for the coming season. While several of the cars have not yet been identified, the one at the right is an early Argyll, built in Alexandria near Loch Lomond.

below: The only surviving example of the Manchester-built Imperial Touring Car, built in 1904 by the Imperial Autocar Manufacturing Company, is now preserved in the city's Museum of Science & Industry.

By the mid-nineteenth century, the transport revolution was well underway with many inventors exploring the potential of steam-powered vehicles. The Grenville Steam Carriage from 1875, now displayed at the National Motor Museum in Beaulieu, Hampshire, is thought to be the oldest steam car still in working order.

But it was the development of the internal combustion engine by Karl Benz in 1879 which kick-started development of petrol-powered personal transport. Benz's first car appeared just five years later in 1884.

British officialdom was initially unimpressed by the motor car – indeed openly antagonistic towards it. The Locomotives Act of 1865 had imposed a speed limit of just 4mph on open roads and just 2mph in towns and there were heavy fines for exceeding that.

When the petrol-engined car came along it, too, was covered by the same legislation and one pioneer, John Henry Knight, was fined five shillings in 1895 for driving his prototype car – actually a powered farm cart – without a traction engine licence, and doing so at 8mph, twice the legal speed limit. He never built another car.

below left: An Albion A6 Tourer from 1909, built in Scotstoun, Glasgow, seen here on the *Time Road* at the British Motor Museum, Gaydon. It was powered by a 5.6 litre side-valve engine. Albion ceased making cars in 1915 to concentrate on commercial vehicles.

below: One of the Albion's acetylene side lamps.

In the closing years of the nineteenth century, several manufacturers, later to become well-known, entered the market. Lanchester produced their first car in 1895, some seven years after Rover had first demonstrated an electric car – more than a century before such ideas really became either practical or fashionable.

German and French manufacturers embraced the new technology much more enthusiastically – thus achieving a significant head start on their British counterparts – with many Renault and Mercedes Benz cars sold in the UK. For several years the majority of London cabs were Renaults.

The early twentieth century saw the likes of Albion, Argyll, Arrol-Johnston, Austin, Morris, Riley, Wolseley and

right: The recreated showroom of Bradburn & Wedge Ltd's Motor Garage at the Black Country Living Museum in Dudley. At the right is a Wolverhampton-built 1903 Sunbeam — the company had started making cars two years earlier — while beyond it stands a 1912 Star Victoria, built by Star Engineering Ltd, also of Wolverhampton.

below: A 1901 10/12hp Arrol-Johnston Dogcart, built in Paisley and displayed at Glasgow's Riverside Museum next to a Glasgow-built Albion A3 12hp from 1904.

below right: The British Motor Museum's 9hp one-litre Riley V-Twin from 1907 had the engine and gearbox under the seat with chain drive to the rear wheels. New, it cost £168 and could reach a speed of 20mph.

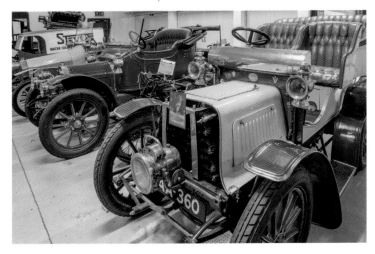

many others enter the market and the industry embarked a period of rapid development both technically and stylistically.

Within two decades of Benz's first success, magnificent vehicles were available to those with deep enough pockets.

Many cars in the early days were sold as 'chassis-only' with the purchaser making separate arrangements with a coach-builder for their chosen vehicle body style.

For Ernest Shackleton's Antarctic expedition in 1907, an Arrol-Johnston was specially built with an air-cooled engine — a water-filled radiator would have been of no use in the frozen Antarctic wastes — and solid rear wheels were fitted with iron strips across them to increase grip, rather like those fitted to contemporary agricultural engines. The front wheels were mounted on skids.

At the top end of the market, coachbuilders like H. J. Mulliner and Park Ward offered a range of customised bodies for Rolls Royces and Bentleys well into the 1950s.

In the early years, hundreds of small manufacturers came and went – some to be absorbed into larger groupings, others simply to disappear after just a few years.

That so many rare models survive today is a testament both to the quality of their manufacture and the subsequent care of their owners and restorers.

On the front of the Bradburn & Wedge motor showroom recreated in Dudley's Black Country Living Museum, the makes and models advertised – most of them also represented in the museum's collection of classic vehicles – include AJS, Bean, Clyno, Star, Sunbeam and Turner, all of them once based in the Dudley and Wolverhampton area, along with Briton, Guy and Stevens.

top: Daimler cars were built in Coventry from 1896, for a time in a former mill building belonging to the Coventry Cotton Spinning and Weaving Company in Radford before a bespoke factory was built.

above: The Wolseley Stellite range first appeared in 1914. This example is in the British Motor Museum.

Of all those, Sunbeam is the only name with which most people today might be familiar, and yet Clyno Engineering was once the third biggest carmaker in Britain, building nearly 40,000 by 1929, and Bean cars outsold both Austin and Morris in the 1920s.

Argyll Motors, who had opened a huge factory at Alexandria near Loch Lomond in 1906, were unusual in supplying complete vehicles at the top end of the market.

Autocar magazine in 1913 noted that 'One need only to state that the body and coachwork are Argyll to convey an impression of excellence.'

The opening of the factory – built at a cost of over £250,000 for the building and the same again to equip it – was widely reported. 'On Tuesday last,' wrote a journalist in *The Graphic* on 30 June 1906, 'an important event in the industrial annals of the Vale of Leven took place in the formal opening of the

below right: Glasgow Riverside Museum's 5hp Argyll Voiture was built in 1900 at the company's Bridgeton Works in Glasgow before the move to the new factory at Alexandria.

below: The interior of a small motor vehicle repair shop, probably in the Glasgow area, photographed c.1900. The car on the right appears to be an Arrol-Johnston Dog-cart, while the vehicle at the left is a De Dion tricycle. By 1902, Arrol-Johnston was a subsidiary of engineers and ship-builders William Beardmore & Company.

new works of Argyll Motors Ltd, at Alexandria. The ceremony was performed by Lord Montagu of Beaulieu, in the presence of a large and distinguished company, the invitations numbering over three hundred. The guests were conveyed from Glasgow and the district around Dumbarton by special train running direct into the Argyll Company's grounds – and for the convenience of visitors from London, a sleeping saloon train was provided.'

All 1500 workers turned out to greet Lord Montagu and, it is said, one of the apprentices was a young man by the name of John Logie Baird. Whatever happened to him?

Argyll's ambitious business plan, however, assumed that there were many more people able to afford between £400 and £800 for a car than turned out to be the case. Despite a lot of advertising and promotion – and the high quality of the cars themselves – the sales volume which

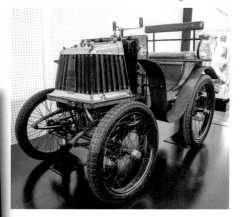

right: The Argyll Motor Works at Alexandria is now a shopping outlet, but the impressive façade which recalls its days as the largest car plant in Europe has been retained. This is the portico over the main entrance.

left: Glasgow's Riverside Museum's 1920 Caledon Model 'E' lorry is the only surviving example.

below: The plates on the dashboard of this 1923 Arrol-Johnston Type D confirm it was built at Heathall near Dumfries and sold in Manchester.

middle: The 1905 Argyll catalogue.

bottom: An advert for the 1908 Argyll 14/16hp model.

would have been necessary for the factory even to cover production costs were never reached.

At £825, the 4 litre 30hp Argyll saloon in 1912 cost eight times a skilled worker's annual pay – more than £200,000 at today's prices – and that £825 is £300 more than a new Mk1 Ford Consul Cortina cost fifty years later.

It would be cheaper cars such as the Model T Ford – built in Manchester from 1911 – and the Longbridge-built Austin 7 from 1922 which really popularised motoring.

The Austin 7 was considered so desirable that it was even manufactured under licence in several other countries, including Germany where it was made by BMW. It is ironic, therefore, that Austin's successor, Austin Rover, would for a time become a subsidiary of BMW – which still owns the 'Mini' brand today. It

is even more ironic that the German-owned Mini brand alone sells more British-built cars today than the entire British-owned Rover Group did in its final years of UK production.

The introduction of the very basic Morris Minor in 1931 brought the price of a car under £100 for the first time – but even that was out of the reach of most people, being the same as the average annual pay for a labourer.

It would not be until the 1960s and '70s that car ownership in Britain really became widespread with the original Mini in its various forms, the Ford Consul Cortina

above: This 1908 Humber car chassis was converted into a flat-bed truck for his own use by a Wigan cabinet-maker c.1913.

above right: At the time of writing, an 11hp Humber Tourer from 1912 was being offered for sale by Essex-based Vintage & Prestige Cars.

middle: A 1932 Model Y Ford stands in the recreated workshop of a typical small country garage from the 1930s at the British Motor Museum, formerly known as the Heritage Motor Centre.

right: The interior of the Cotswold Motor Museum in Bourton-on-the-Water in Gloucestershire. The museum has one of the world's largest collection of motoring advertising signage.

and others achieving mass sales. The Cortina in its various forms went on to sell more than 2.5 million in Britain, beaten in the all-time top ten by the Vauxhall Astra, the Ford Escort and, top of the list, the Ford Fiesta.

One of the most iconic of British brands – Jaguar – went through several name changes before the marque we know today emerged. Starting life as the Swallow Sidecar Company, set up in Blackpool in 1922 by William Lyons and William Walmsley, the name was changed to SS Cars Ltd in 1934, by which time they had relocated to the Midlands.

Nobody could have imagined just what unfortunate associations that decision would bring within just a few years. One of their models, the *SS Jaguar* gave them their new name, the company becoming Jaguar Cars in 1945.

While the story of the road vehicle has been dominated by petrol and diesel power for much of the last century, a lot of what we might still consider to be 'new technology' as far as cars are concerned has been around for a very long time, perhaps just waiting for it to be developed to a level where it is truly viable.

For electric cars, that moment is nigh, although that prediction has been being made for more than a century.

A report in the *Sydney Morning Herald* in June 1901 commented that 'If anything were wanting to invest the pastime of motoring with greater popularity in ladies' eyes it is surely supplied by the fact that Queen Alexandra has not only purchased for herself a Victoriette, but has learned to drive it herself. Electricity is the main motive force of the extremely smart little vehicle, with seats for two, that Her Majesty has selected.'

above left: The 1934 SS One Airline, one of the first models launched after the company's name was changed.

above: The 1936 MG SA, the first large car to carry the MG badge, was powered by a 78bhp 2.3 litre 6-cylinder engine.

right: One of the workshops at Vauxhall's Luton factory in the 1920s. The company had been established by Scottish engineer Alexander Wilson in Vauxhall, London, in 1857, making marine engines before launching its first car in 1903 — a single-cylinder 5hp model. The business was moved to Luton in 1905 trading as Vauxhall Iron Works, a name it retained until 1908 when it became Vauxhall Motors, three years after it had become a subsidiary of the American General Motors. Several of its early cars and lorries incorporated components from its American parent's Chevrolet models.

below: Once-familiar sights on British roads, a Thornycroft Nippy, built in Southampton in 1949, stands alongside a 1959 ERF Box Van at the Westbury Vintage Gathering in Wiltshire. Pioneer of steam wagons, Edwin Richard Foden had fallen out with his fellow directors at Foden Motors in Sandbach, Cheshire, who in the economic downturn of the early 1930s, had seen no future in diesel lorries. The ERF name continued to be used on trucks until 1981.

The American-built Victoriette had a claimed range of 40-50 miles between charges, something it would take battery technology many years to exceed.

Way back in 1903 *Autocar* magazine produced a catalogue to accompany Britain's first motor show, and in addition to the many petrol-driven models and a range of steam-powered vehicles, the catalogue listed four electric carriages, two of which claimed a range for 45-50 miles on a single battery charge. More than sixty years later, the ill-fated Scamp electric car, built in Prestwick by Scottish Aviation, could

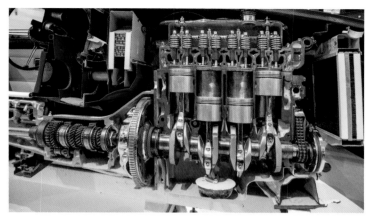

left: A cut-away of the 98bhp 4-cylinder 1798cc engine in the 1965 MGB Roadster — referred to at the time as the 'poor man's Aston Martin' — displayed at the British Motor Museum, Gaydon.

below: The Scamp was a failed electric car project built by Scottish Aviation in Prestwick in 1965.

manage only 20 miles on a charge. Only a dozen or so prototypes were ever built.

Could hydrogen power, or even steam be the future for ecologically sound motoring? Steam is no longer the heavy system it once was.

The Grenville Steam Carriage on display at Beaulieu is believed to be the oldest working self-propelled vehicle in the world. Built by Robert Neville Grenville of Glastonbury, Somerset, in 1875, the vehicle was originally fitted with a single-cylinder steam engine but this was replaced almost immediately with a twin-cylinder unit. It trundled along at just a few miles per hour

More than 125 years later, the fastest steam-powered vehicle in the world, the 2009 British Steam Car – also on show at Beaulieu – gained the world record having achieved an average speed of 148.166mph over a measured mile.

That pales into near-insignificance when compared with the record for a hydrogen cell car at 280.007mph set in 2008. By mid 2016 hydrogen-powered cars were available from Honda, Hyundai and Toyota, all of them very expensive.

The 1892 Manchester-built Model 1 was the first linotype machine to be built in Britain by the Linotype Company Ltd.

GAZETTEER
PAPER AND PRINT

Amberley Museum
www.amberleymuseum.co.uk tel: 01798 831370 Station Road, Amberley, Near Arundel, West Sussex, BN18 9LT This extensive museum has a working printworks with recently-restored Linotype machines, a treadle platen, Adana presses and a Columbia Press. There are regular demonstrations of typesetting and printing. Open daily in school holidays, and Wednesday-Sunday at other times. Admission charge.

Cambridge Museum of Technology
www.museumoftechnology.com tel: 01223 500652 The Old Pumping Station, Cheddars Lane, Cambridge CB5 8LD Housed in a preserved Victorian steam pumping station, the museum has a large collection of presses using wood & metal type, and Linotype, Ludlow and Monotype casters. Open Sundays only, check website for details. Admission charge.

Apsley Paper Trail/Frogmore Paper Mill
www.thepapertrail.org.uk tel: 01442 234600 Fourdrinier Way, Hemel Hempstead, Hertfordshire HP3 9RY The world's oldest mechanised paper mill is still a working paper mill producing paper on historic machines. The museum also has an extensive collection of vintage printing equipment, *see opposite*. The mill is open every Thursday and the first Sunday of each month from 11am-4pm. Admission charge.

John Jarrold Printing Museum
www.johnjarroldprintingmuseum.org.uk tel: 01603 677183 Whitefriars Norwich Norfolk NR3 1SH Working collection of nineteenth and twentieth century printing equipment with demonstrations and 'hands-on' opportunities. Limited opening – check website. Admissions charge.

MOSI Manchester
www.mosi.org.uk tel: 0161 832 2244 Liverpool Road, Castlefield, Manchester, M3 4FP The Museum of Science & Industry covers a wide range of themes focusing on, amongst other things, Manchester's contribution to the world of print and the wider world of communications, including the first British-built Linotype machine which revolutionised the newspaper industry. Open daily. Free admission.

Robert Smail's Printing Works
www.nts.org.uk/Property/robert-smails-printing-works tel: 0844 493 2259 7/9 High Street, Innerleithen, Peebles, EH44 6HA Preserved print works still used for commercial jobs, including some of the NTS's own literature. Visitors can experience composing and printing. Presses. Open April to October, Friday, Saturday and Monday 11am-5pm. Sunday 1-5pm. Admission charge.

Wookey Hole Hand-Made Paper Mill
www.wookey.co.uk tel: 01749 672243 The Mill, High St, Wookey Hole, Wells, Somerset BA5 1BB A paper mill since the seventeenth century, visitors can watch the Vatman and his assistant, the Coucher, making paper in the traditional way and then have a go at making some paper themselves. Open daily. Admission charge.

THE FARMING INDUSTRY

Avoncroft Museum of Historic Buildings
www.avoncroft.org.uk tel: 01527 831363 Stoke Heath, Bromsgrove, Worcestershire B60 4JR An eclectic collection of rescued buildings spanning centuries of British domestic and commercial architecture – everything from timber-framed buildings to the post-war asbestos prefab – all reassembled on a single site. This is the story of centuries of rural British architecture in microcosm. Check website for opening times. Admission charge.

Chiltern Open Air Museum
www.coam.org.uk tel: 01494 871117 Newland Park, Gorelands Lane, Chalfont St Giles, Buckinghamshire HP8 4AB The museum's farm buildings replicate a Chilterns farmstead between 1800 and 1950 and are filled with equipment across the timescale. The farmstead is also the base for a programme of conservation and restoration of historic equipment, much of which is in action throughout the year. Open late March to October. Admission charge.

Essex Country Show
www.barleylands.co.uk tel: 01268 290228 Barleylands Farm, Barleylands Road, Billericay CM11 2UD 2-day event in September including demonstrations of both farming with heavy horses and with steam. Many steam engines on display and at work. Check website for dates. Admission charge.

Great Dorset Steam Fair
www.gdsf.co.uk tel: 01258 860361 South Down, Tarrant Hinton, Blandford, Dorset DT11 8HX Britain's most famous – and largest – steam fair, held over five days, usually in late August. The fair covers an enormous showground and at over 600 acres is Europe's largest steam event. Numerous steam farming demonstrations and displays are a feature of the event. Check website for dates. Admission charge.

Hollycombe Collection
www.hollycombe.co.uk tel: 01428 724900 Iron Hill, Liphook, Hampshire, GU30 7LP Working farm engines, road engines, maritime engines and steam fairground rides. Open April to October most weekends, and Weds-Suns in August. Occasional demonstrations of steam farming include two ploughing engines – the Fowler BB class *Prince* and the unique John Allen & Sons (Oxford) Ltd engine – and steam threshing demonstrations. Check website for steaming dates. Admission charge.

Murton Park Yorkshire Museum of Farming
www.murtonpark.co.uk tel: 01904 489966 Murton, York, YO19 5UF The museum's collection tells the story of Yorkshire faming from the earliest time to the present day, with a wide range of historic vehicles and implements displayed in two large exhibition halls. Open Easter to October. Admission charge.

Museum of East Anglian Life
www.eastanglianlife.org.uk tel: 01449 612229 Illife Way, Stowmarket, Suffolk, IP14 1DL A large museum set in a 75 acre site, with 17 splendidly restored historic buildings including a working watermill and Victorian tin tabernacle. Occasional open days including farming demonstrations – see website. Admission charge.

THE FARMING INDUSTRY

National Museum of Rural Life

www.nts.org.uk/Property/National-Museum-of-Rural-Life tel: 0300 123 6789
Philipshill Road, East Kilbride, G76 9HR A unique partnership between the National
Trust for Scotland and National Museums Scotland, the museum has large exhibition
halls containing displays of artifacts from Scotland's farming history, with a farm
which is still worked using techniques and equipment from the 1950s. Open daily.
Admission charge.

The Steam Museum

www.thesteammuseum.org tel: 01227 722502 Preston, Canterbury, Kent CT3 1DH
The Steam Museum's extensive collection embraces road engines, farm engines and
associated farm equipment, together with early nineteenth century steam-powered
wooden fairground rides. Currently under restoration at Ramsgate is the museum's
steam tug *Cervia*. The Museum site is only accessible to the public on advertised
Open Days, so check website for details. Admission charge.

Torbay Steam Fair

www.torbaysteamfair.co.uk tel: 07990 9830721 Dartmouth Road, Churston Ferrers,
Brixham, Devon, TQ5 0JT Three day event in August. Farming with steam –
demonstrations of wood cutting, threshing, hauling, ploughing, etc. Also fairground
rides and organs, motorcycles and military vehicles. Check website for dates.
Admission charge.

Oakham Treasures Tractor and Farm Museum

www.oakhamtreasures.co.uk tel: 01275 375236 Oakham Farm, Portbury Lane,
Portbury, Bristol BS20 7SP The museum has a collection of over one hundred and fifty
tractors on display together with other farming implements, the oldest – a Fordson –
dating back to 1918. There is also a collection of old gas and oil-fired farm engines
some dating back more than a century. Oakham Treasures has a collection of several
diverse museums on the same site. Open Tuesday to Saturday. Admission charge.

Weald & Downland Open Air Museum

www.wealddown.co.uk tel: 01243 811363 Singleton, Chichester, West Sussex, PO18
0EU A collection of more than 50 buildings, spanning more than 600 years, rescued
from sites across southern England, including workers' cottages, shops, farmhouses,
barns, a watermill, and even a church. The museum also offers a programme of
demonstrations, including blacksmithing, milling, pole-lathe turning and scything
and, occasionally, traditional building techniques such as lead working,
stonemasonry, lime slaking, thatching or wattle-and-daubing. Open daily from
March to mid-December. Admission charge.

Wiltshire Steam & Vintage Rally

www.wapg.co.uk tel: 01672 563525 Rainscombe Park, Oare, Marlborough, Wiltshire
SN8 4HZ The Wiltshire Agricultural Preservation Group organises a number of events
throughout the year but their two-day June rally brings together a large gathering of
vintage farm and other equipment including agricultural engines, tractors, commercial
and military vehicles, and demonstrations of steam ploughing and other activities.

CHINA, TILES AND GLASS

Alloa Northern Glass Cone
42 Craigward, Alloa FK10 1NU Category A listed octagonal-based 25m tall brick-built cone dating from around 1825 and now the only surviving glass cone in Scotland. It stands in the middle of the Alloa Glass Works site. Exterior viewable.

Catcliffe Glass Cone
Off Tristford Close, Catcliffe, Rotherham S60 5JG Built around 1740 for William Fenny's Glassworks. The oldest surviving glass cone in Europe, it is now virtually surrounded by a housing estate. The cone is currently undergoing stabilisation and restoration. Exterior viewable.

Coalport China Museum
www.ironbridge.org.uk/our-attractions/coalport-china-museum tel: 01952 580650 High St, Telford TF8 7HT Part of the Ironbridge Gorge World Heritage Site, the museum tells the story of Coalport China, between 1795 and 1926. Demonstrations of ceramic techniques. Original industrial buildings including bottle ovens. Open daily. Admission charge.

Gladstone Pottery Museum
www.stokemuseums.org.uk/visit/gpm tel: 01782 237777 Uttoxeter Road, Longton, Stoke-on-Trent, ST3 1PQ Bone china ware was made in the workshops and giant bottle kilns of the Gladstone China Works, the last complete Victorian pottery factory in the country. Includes collection of sanitary ware, including some made by the legendary Thomas Crapper. Four large bottle ovens dominate the site. Daily demonstrations of bone china flower making, pot throwing and ceramic painting. Open Tues-Sat and Bank Holidays. Admission charge.

Jackfield Tile Museum
www.ironbridge.org.uk/our-attractions/jackfield-tile-museum tel: 01952 433424 Salthouse Rd, Ironbridge, Shropshire TF8 7LJ Part of the Ironbridge Gorge World Heritage Site, the museum in the former Craven Dunnill Tile Works displays decorative tiles spanning the period 1840 to 1960 when the local tile industry was at is height. Regular tile-making demonstrations. Open daily. Admission Charge.

Lemington Glass Cone
www.stanegatestoves.co.uk tel: 0191 267 7100 Stanegate Stoves Ltd, The Cone, The Old Glassworks, Lemington, Newcastle upon Tyne, NE15 8SX Now used as the showrooms for a stoves company the cone, which was built in 1787, is the only survivor of four built by the Northumberland Glass Company to produce sheet glass on the site.

Middleport Pottery
www.middleportpottery.org tel: 01782 499766 Port Street, Burslem, Stoke-on-Trent, ST6 3PE The Middleport Pottery Museum and factory tour offers the chance to see pottery being made using the same handcraft methods as in the 1880s. The tour takes visitors through the entire process from a lump of clay to finished pottery. Visitors can also see the steam engine which once powered the whole factory. Tours currently cost £7.50 and must be booked in advance, but access to the visitor cente is free. Open daily 10am-4pm.

CHINA, TILES AND GLASS

National Glass Centre
www.nationalglasscentre.com tel: 0191 515 5555 Liberty Way, Sunderland, SR6 0GL
A centre for research and part of the University of Sunderland, the Glass Centre has a museum on the history of glass-making and is host to a programme of exhibitions. Daily demonstrations of glass blowing. Open daily, free admission.

Red House Glass Cone
www.dudley.gov.uk/see-and-do/museums/red-house-glass-cone/ tel: 01384 812750
High Street, Wordsley, Stourbridge, West Midlands, DY8 4AZ 100 feet high glass cones were commonplace in the Stourbridge area. Today, this is the only complete glass cone in the area and one of only four left in the United Kingdom. The Red House Glass Cone was built at the end of the eighteenth century and was used for the manufacture of glass until 1936. The museum tells the story of 200 years of glass-making. Open daily 10am-4pm, admission free.

Rosedale Glass Furnace
www.ryedalefolkmuseum.co.uk tel: 01751 417367 Ryedale Folk Museum, Hutton le Hole, North Yorkshire, YO62 6UA This rare survival of a sixteenth century glass furnace was discovered in Rosedale in the 1960s and rebuilt at the Ryedale Folk Museum. The furnace was probably built by Hugenot refugees – its design is similar to surviving furnaces in France. Now part of the extensive Ryedale site, the furnace would originally have had adjacent annealing chambers. Open March to October. Admission charge.

Somerset Brick and Tile Museum
www.swheritage.org.uk/brick--tile-museum tel: 01278 426088 East Quay, Bridgwater, Somerset, TA6 4AE The museum is dedicated to one of the many labour-intensive coal-based industries once found in most Somerset towns. It is centred on the last tile kiln in Bridgwater, now scheduled as a Grade II* ancient monument, and last fired in 1965. There are regular demonstrations of how bricks, tiles, terracotta plaques and other wares were made. Open Tuesday and Thursday only. Admission charge.

The Stained Glass Museum
www.stainedglassmuseum.com tel: 01353 660347 The South Triforium, Ely Cathedral, Ely, Cambridgeshire, CB7 4DL The museum has a collection of over 125 stained glass panels covering 800 years of craftsmanship, all displayed at eye level to give a unique close-up view. There are also extensive displays of the tools and materials used in the design and manufacture of glass, lead and stained glass windows. Open daily Monday to Saturday, Sundays pm only.

The World of Glass
www.worldofglass.com tel: 01744 22766 Chalon Way East, St Helens, Merseyside, WA10 1BX A large museum charting the story of glass in general, and St Helens as a centre of the industry in particular. Built on the site of a former iron foundry and a glassworks, the museum is entered through a replica of a glass cone kiln. Contains the underground tunnels of the worlds' first regenerative glass making furnace built in 1887 by William Windle Pilkington. Regular demonstrations of glass blowing. Permanent galleries and changing exhibitions. Open Monday to Saturday, all year round, admission charge.

Thursford's Wellershaus
Fairground Organ,
built 1900-1910.

ALL THE FUN OF THE FAIR

Beamish Museum
www.beamish.org.uk tel: 0191 370 4000 Beamish, County Durham, DH9 0RG The centerpiece of the fairground at Beamish Edwardian town is the 1893 set of steam Gallopers built for William Beach by Savage of Kings Lynn. The ride was owned by the Beach family for 113 years and still has all of its original, hand-carved wooden horses, along with its steam centre engine, *May Queen*, and an 89 key Gavioli organ. Check website for opening times. Admission charge.

Black Country Living Museum
www.bclm.com tel: 0121 557 9643 Tipton Road, Dudley, West Midlands, DY1 4SQ Since it opened in 1983, the museum's Edwardian fair, with its historic rides, has been operated by the third and fourth generation of the Jones family of Cradley Heath who started travelling with the fairs in the early 1900s. Open daily March/April to October. Check website for details. Admission charge.

Blists Hill Victorian Town
www.ironbridge.org.uk/our-attractions/blists-hill-victorian-town tel: 01952 433424 Legges Way, Madeley, Telford, Shropshire TF7 5DU During the summer season, Blists Hill operates a Victorian fairground with assorted rides and amusements. The fairground's centrepiece, the Harris & Scrivens Steam Gallopers, was built by Thomas Walker of Tewkesbury in 1911. Open daily. Admission charge.

Bressingham Gallopers
www.bressingham.co.uk tel: 01379 686900 Bressingham Steam Museum, Gardens and Garden Centre, Diss, Norfolk, IP22 2AA Bressingham's three-abreast Gallopers were built by Savages of Kings Lynn in 1897 and owned and operated by the Thurston family of Norfolk until 1934. The steam centre engine was built by Robert Tidman & Sons of Norwich. Bressingham also has an important collection of steam locomotives in both standard gauge and narrow gauge, some working, others on display only. Open 10am to 5.30pm daily from the end of March to the end of October. Admission charge.

Carters Steam Fairs
www.carterssteamfair.co.uk tel: 01628 822221 Carters organise up to 20 steam fairs, mostly held at venues around London and the south of England between April and October, with occasional venues as far west as Bath. See website for details. Their rides include early steam-powered gallopers and steam yachts, alongside a wide range of Edwardian electric-driven rides and sideshows, all beautifully restored and returned to working order.

Dingles Fairground Heritage Centre
www.fairground-heritage.org.uk tel: 01566 783425 Milford, Lifton, Devon, PL16 0AT Home of the National Fairground Collection, the museum has an extensive collection of early fairground rides and organs, engines and ephemera. The Rodeo Switchback is the last remaining Spinning Top Switchback in the world, and is believed to be the oldest surviving fairground ride in the country. Lots of live steam at the Autumn Fairground Weekend in late September. Open daily mid-March to end of October. Admission charge.

ALL THE FUN OF THE FAIR

Folly Farm Vintage Funfair

www.folly-farm.co.uk tel: 01834 812731 Begelly, Kilgetty, Pembrokeshire, SA68 0XA
Large indoor fairground with various rides, sideshows and attractions, including
what is believed to be the last set of three-abreast Gallopers built by Frederick Savage
of King's Lynn in 1922. Open daily, February to November. Weekends only during
winter. Admission charge.

Great Dorset Steam Fair

www.gdsf.co.uk tel: 01258 860361 South Down, Tarrant Hinton, Blandford, Dorset
DT11 8HX Britain's most famous, and largest, steam fair, held over five days in late
August and early September attracts hundreds of participants and thousands of
visitors. Steam fairground rides are a major feature of the event when numerous
travelling fairs take part. Admission charge.

Hollycombe Steam in the Country

www.hollycombe.co.uk tel: 01428 724900 Iron Hill, Liphook, Hampshire, GU30 7LP
An amazing collection of working steam engines including railway locomotives,
farm engines, road engines, maritime engines, and steam fairground rides.
Hollycombe's three-abreast Steam Gallopers, built around 1912 by Tidman of
Norwich, – with 24 horses, six cockerels and two chariots – are driven by a Tidman
steam centre engine, and the revolving pillars, believed to be the only ones still
operating, are driven by a Tidman organ engine. Open April to October most
weekends, and Wednesdays to Sundays in August. Two-day steam rally late May.
Check website for details of all steaming dates. Admission charge.

Scarborough Fair Collection

www.scarboroughfaircollection.com tel: 01723 586698 Flower of May Holiday Park,
Scarborough, North Yorks. YO11 3NU This huge collection of showmen's steam
engines and fairground rides includes a set of Tidman Gallopers, a rare Caterpillar
ride, many other vintage fairground attractions, assembled by Graham Atkinson. The
collection includes some unique survivals of steam lorries – amongst them a rare
1908 Foden Steam Wagon. Open Wednesday to Sundays March to October,
Wednesdays only out of season. Admission charge.

The Steam Museum

www.thesteammuseum.org tel: 01227 722502 Preston, Canterbury, Kent CT3 1DH
Alongside many steam engines, the museum is home to a collection of early
nineteenth century wooden fairground rides and equipment. The most spectacular of
these is the Thomas Walker three-abreast steam-driven Gallopers set currently in the
process of restoration. Built in Tewksbury in 1911, the gallopers have their original
carved wooden horses by Andersons of Bristol, a Verbeek 89 key organ and a very
rare Walker steam centre engine. Check website for open days. Admission charge.

Thursford Collection

www.thursford.com tel: 01328 878477 Thursford, Fakenham, Norfolk, NR21 0AS
Stunning collection of vintage fairground rides and fairground organs together with
Showmen's Engines and farm engines. On display is a very early Savage centre
engine, Savage's venetian Gondola Swithback, and three-abreast Gallopers. Open
April to September, closed Fridays and Saturdays. Admission charge.

COMMUNICATIONS

Amberley Museum
www.amberleymuseum.co.uk tel: 01798 831370 Station Road, Amberley, Near Arundel, West Sussex, BN18 9LT This extensive museum has a Space and Telecommunications Hall which covers many aspects of early communication technologies including an amateur radio station. Open daily during school holidays and Wednesday to Sunday at other times. Check website for opening times. Admission charge.

Bletchley Park
www.bletchleypark.org.uk tel: 01908 640404 Milton Keynes, MK3 6EB The birthplace of British code-breaking, Bletchley Park was once one of Britain's best kept secrets, but is now recognised throughout the world as a site of major importance. Visitors explore the world of the code-breakers and can see many of the electro-mechanical machines used to intercept and decipher enemy communications during World War II. Open daily except Christmas. Admission charge.

British Vintage Wireless and Television Museum
www.bvwm.org.uk tel: 020 8670 3667 23 Rosendale Road, West Dulwich, London, SE21 8DS   A Victorian house packed with hundreds of vintage radios and televisions assembled by the late Gerald Wells. The museum is currently undergoing a reorganisation. Open by appointment. Check website for details.

Goonhilly Satellite Earth Station
www.goonhilly.org tel: 0800 043 7768 Goonhilly Downs, Helston, Cornwall TR12 6LQ The station which received the first ever live pictures by satellite from the USA in 1962, is undergoing a major upgrade, and a new visitor centre will explore Goonhilly's role in the development of satellite transmission, and the its current role in the science of space exploration. Check website for latest information.

Jodrell Bank Discovery Centre
www.jodrellbank.net tel: 01477 571766 The University of Manchester, Macclesfield, Cheshire, SK11 9DL Home of the Lovell Radio Telescopethe site now includes special exhibitions on the history of radio astronomy, the exploration of deep space, and the emergence of the science which underpins it all. Open daily. Admission charge.

Lizard Wireless
www.lizardwireless.org tel: 01326 291174 The Lizard, Cornwall. The Lizard Wireless Station was set up by the Marconi Company at the end of 1900 to supply a ship-to-shore radio service with ships passing Lizard Point. It is operates an amateur radio licence and demonstrations are available.The museum is in the original buildings, restored to their 1900 appearance. Limited opening times so check website. A challenging walk is involved.

Museum of Communication
www.mocft.co.uk tel: 01592 874836 131 High Street, Burntisland, Fife, KY3 9AA The museum offers extensive displays of telegraphy, telephony, audio, radio, television and video and IT. The collection includes experimental radar and satellite equipment. Open May to September. Tuesdays and Saturdays, some other times by appointment. Admission free.

COMMUNICATIONS

National Media Museum
www.nationalmediamuseum.org.uk tel: 0844 856 3797 Little Horton Lane, Bradford, West Yorkshire BD1 1NQ   The museum tells the stories of photography, film and television in a series of interactive galleries and exhibitions. The television galleries explore the history of television, from the first scientific breakthrough in 1877 to the evolution of colour transmissions, recording devices and satellite television. Open daily, Free Admission.

National Museum of Computing
www.tnmoc.org tel: 01908 374708 Block H, Bletchley Park, Milton Keynes, MK3 6EB The museum has some of the earliest mechanical machines, early electro-mechanical devices in use in deciphering communications during World War II, and major developments since then. Admission charge. See website for opening times.

Orkney Wireless Museum
www.orkneywirelessmuseum.org.uk tel: 01856 871400 Kiln Corner, Junction Road, Kirkwall, Orkney, KW15 1LB   The displays and photographic archive tell of the strategic importance of Orkney during World War II. The museum demonstrates the importance of wireless communications and radar in both civilian and military circles. Open daily April to October.

RAF Air Defence Radar Museum
www.radarmuseum.co.uk tel: 01692 631485 Nr RRH Neatishead, Horning, Norfolk, NR12 8YB   The museum, on the site of the world's longest continuously operating radar station which opened in 1941, provides a unique window into the history of radar. Open Tuesdays, Thursdays and Bank Holiday Mondays, April to October inclusive, and the second Saturday of each month. Admission charge.

The Signals Museum RAF Henlow
www.rafsignalsmuseum.org.uk tel: 01462 851515 Building 104, RAF Henlow, Beds, SG16 6DN   Most of the items on display come from WW2 and the pre-war period, the early days of radio. Open to the public on the first Saturday of each month except January. Suitable ID must be presented at the guard post – check website for details.

The Telegraph Museum
www.porthcurno.org.uk tel: 01736 810966 Eastern House, Porthcurno, Cornwall TR19 6JX   Porthcurno Telegraph Station became a hub of global communications in Victorian times. 14 undersea cables connected it to every corner of the Earth. The station's historic buildings have been restored and filled with collections chronicling the evolution of global communications, including undersea cables, the stories of the ships which laid them, and a working recreation of a 1920s telegraph station. Open daily in summer, weekends and Mondays in winter. Admission charge.

Washford Radio Museum
www.tropiquaria.co.uk/washfordradiomuseum.html tel: 01984 640688 Tropiquaria, Washford Cross, Watchet, Somerset, TA23 0QB   The Museum is part of Tropiquaria wildlife park, which is housed in the Art Deco former BBC Transmitting Station, built in 1933. Its collections cover ninety years of radio and television history. Opening days and times vary so check website. Admission charge.

ROADS AND BRIDGES

British Motor Museum
www.britishmotormuseum.co.uk tel: 01926 641188 Banbury Road, Gaydon, Warwickshire, CV35 0BJ The museum's 'Time Road' is an innovative way of explaining how, as vehicles developed, the roads on which they ran were also improved – from the dust and rubble roads of the Victorian era to the smooth surfaces of today. The cars displayed along the 'Time Road' stand on surfaces which are typical of the time when they were built. Open daily. Admission charge.

Clifton Bridge Visitor Centre
www.cliftonbridge.org.uk tel: 0117 974 4664 Bridgemaster's Office, Bridge Rd, Bristol, North Somerset BS8 3PA The Visitor Centre is situated at the Leigh Woods end of Brunel's bridge and contains illustrated displays on the bridge's design and construction. The bridge has been entirely funded by tolls since it opened in 1864. Free admission. Open 10am-5pm daily except Christmas and New Year.

Menai Heritage/Thomas Telford Centre
www.menaibridges.co.uk tel: 01248 715046 Mona Road, Menai Bridge, Anglesey, LL59 5EA Small community museum celebrating Telford's Menai Suspension Bridge, and Robert Stephenson's Britannia Bridge. Open Wednesday and Thursday, April to November. The museum is located about 300 metres from the waterfront. Admission charge.

Newport Transporter Bridge Visitor Centre
www.fontb.org.uk tel: 01633 656656 64 Cardiff Rd, Newport NP20 2UA The Visitor Centre tells the story of the French-designed bridge from its construction and opening in 1906. Open April to September, but check the website for precise bridge operating times and Visitor Centre opening times. A 'Day Ticket', currently costing just £3, allows unlimited use of the bridge and access to the high-level walkway.

Tees Transporter Bridge Visitor Centre
www.middlesbrough.gov.uk tel: 01642 727265 Ferry Road, Middlesbrough TS2 1PL The visitor centre promotes the history of the bridge and surrounding area through the use of graphic panels, video, computers, photographs, objects and models, and tells the story of the industrial heritage of Middlesbrough, a major player in the Industrial Revolution, and especially shipping. For opening times check website.

The Forth Bridge Experience
www.forthbridgeexperience.com South Queensferry, EH30 9SF At the time of writing there are plans under evaluation to create a Visitor Centre at the base of the Fife cantilever of the UNESCO World Heritage Site, with lift access to the highest level of the bridge. There will be regular progress updates on the website.

Tower Bridge Exhibition
www.towerbridge.org.uk tel: 020 7403 3761 Tower Bridge Road, London, SE1 2UP A chance to explore the iconic bridge and walk across the glass walkway on the upper level. The exhibition describing how the bridge was built can be found in the south tower and along the upper walkway. Also open are the Victorian engine rooms below the road on the north side of the river, the engines beautifully restored. Open daily. Admission charge.

ROAD TRANSPORT

Atwell-Wilson Motor Museum
www.atwellwilson.org.uk   tel: 01249 813119   Stockley Lane, Calne , Wiltshire, SN11 0NF   The museum has over 100 exhibits, the majority of which are cars from the 1920s onwards, together with a collection of motorcycles, mopeds, bicycles, motoring memorabilia and a reconstructed 1930s-style garage complete with cars. Open Tuesdays to Sundays April to October, Thursdays to Sundays November to March. Admission charge.

Black Country Living Museum
www.bclm.com   tel: 0121 5579643   Tipton Road, Dudley, DY1 4SQ   Recreation of a small Edwardian town by the side of the Dudley Canal. Collections include rare locally-built vehicles and more on a 26-acre industrial site. Two single-deck trams of c.1920 and a 1909 double-deck open-topped Wolverhampton tram run on the 3'6" gauge tramway. Open daily March/April to October. Admission charge.

British Commercial Vehicle Museum
www.britishcommercialvehiclemuseum.com tel: 01772 451011 King Street, Leyland, Lancashire PR25 2LE   The museum's collection of over 60 vehicles ranges from the horse-drawn transport of the 1880s through steam wagons, and petrol and diesel powered lorries and buses. A number of special events are held each year – check website for details. Open Thursday to Sunday from April to the end of October. Admission charge.

British Motor Museum
www.britishmotormuseum.co.uk tel: 01926 641188 Banbury Road, Gaydon, Warwickshire, CV35 0BJ Formerly the Heritage Motor Centre and recently re-branded, the British Motor Industry Heritage Trust's collection of over 300 British-built cars chronicling the history of the British motor industry from Albion in 1901 to the last-ever Rover 75 in 2005. Open daily. Admission charge.

Brooklands Museum
www.brooklandsmuseum.com tel: 01932 857381 Brooklands Road, Weybridge, Surrey, KT13 0QN   Museum of transport, motor sport and aviation. Large collection of cars, and the London Bus Museum contains around 35 buses and coaches, the largest collection of historic London buses in the world. Open daily except Christmas. Admission charge.

Cotswold Motor Museum
www.cotswoldmotoringmuseum.co.uk tel: 01451 821255 The Old Mill, Sherborne St, Bourton-on-the-Water, Gloucestershire GL54 2BY   The museum's collection includes cars, motorcycles, bicycles, caravans, enamel signage and twentieth century motoring memorabilia. Open daily mid-February to mid-December. Admission charge.

Coventry Transport Museum
www.transport-museum.com tel: 024 7623 4270 Millennium Place, Hales Street, Coventry CV1 1JD The collection consists of motor cars, commercial vehicles, cycles and motorcycles over the past 150 years – during which time 475 bicycle and tricycle makers, 161 car manufacturers and 116 motorcycle manufacturers operated in the city. Open daily 10am-5pm. Admission free.

ROAD TRANSPORT

Crich Tramway Village
www.tramway.co.uk tel: 01773 854321 The National Tramway Museum, Crich, Nr. Matlock, Derbyshire, DE4 5DP   The museum has the largest collection of trams in Britain, from the horse-drawn vehicles of the 1860s through to the electric trams of the 1960s. Some of the trams run along a mile-long scenic route, past a recreated Edwardian shopping street. Open March to October. Admission charge.

Glasgow Riverside Museum
www.glasgowmuseums.com/riverside/pages/default.aspx tel: 0141 287 2720 100 Pointhouse Road, Glasgow G3 8RS Built on the site of the former Pointhouse Shipyard, the museum contains a wealth of information on the city's transport history and includes a large and unrivalled collection of Scottish-built cars and lorries. The Clyde-built sailing ship *Glenlee* is moored at the quayside. Open daily. Free admission.

Grampian Transport Museum
www.gtm.org.uk tel: 01975 562292 Montgarrie Rd, Alford AB33 8AE   The collection includes the only surviving example of a Glasgow-built Sentinel Steam Waggon, built in 1914 shortly before the company relocated to Shrewsbury. It is still occasionally steamed. Also in the collection is the 'Craigievar Express' steam vehicle built by a local postman in 1895. The museum also mounts changing exhibitions on motoring history. Open daily April to October 10am-5pm. Admission charge.

Greater Manchester Museum of Transport
www.mts.co.uk   tel: 0161 205 2122 Museum of Transport, Boyle Street, Cheetham, Manchester M8 8UW Based in one of Manchester's earliest bus garages, adjoining the city's first electric tram depot, the Museum tells the story of public road transport in Manchester from 1824 to the present day. The collection spans over 100 years, from an 1890s horse bus to a full size prototype Metrolink tram. Open Wednesday to Sunday, and daily in August. Admission charge.

Haynes International Motor Museum
www.haynesmotormuseum.com tel: 01963 440804 Sparkford, Yeovil, Somerset, BA22 7LH   The collection includes over 400 cars and motorcycles from all over the world. The site is currently being expanded to increase exhibition space. Open daily. Admission charge.

Lakeland Motor Museum
www.lakelandmotormuseum.co.uk tel: 015395 30400 Old Blue Mill, Backbarrow, Ulverston, Cumbria LA12 8TA As well as an eclectic mix of cars, the museum is home to a diverse collection of 30,000 pieces of motoring ephemera assembled over a period of almost fifty years and a recreation of a local Lakeland garage in the 1930s. Open daily except Christmas Day. Admission charge.

Levens Hall Collection
www.levenshall.co.uk tel: 01539 560321 Levens Hall, Kendal, Cumbria, LA8 0PD The collection at Levens Hall, assembled by Robin and Hal Bagot, includes a 1925 Foden Steam Wagon, a 1902 Locke Steam Car, the Fowler 1920 Showman's Road Locomotive *Bertha*, and a half-size Traction Engine, *Little Gem*, the last two in steam. Open Sundays to Thursdays, April to October. Admission charge.

ROAD TRANSPORT

London Bus Museum
www.londonbusmuseum.com tel: 01932 837994 Brooklands Road, Weybridge, Surrey, KT13 0QN The largest collection of London buses in the world and includes vehicles from a London General Omnibus Company's horse-bus from the mid 1870s through to the 70-seaters of the 1970s. Formerly the Cobham Bus Museum, the collection was moved to new custom-built premises in 2011 and is open seven days a week except Christmas, 10am-5pm in summer, 4pm in winter. Admission charge.

London Transport Museum
www.ltmuseum.co.uk tel: 020 7379 6344 Covent Garden Piazza, London WC2E 7BB The collection was started the 1920s, when the London General Omnibus Company preserved two Victorian horse buses and an early motorbus. The museum is housed in the Flower Market building in Covent Garden and includes buses, trams, and a cross section of London's overground and underground transport. Open daily. Admission charge.

Milestones Museum
www.hampshireculturaltrust.org.uk/milestones-museum tel: 01256 639550 Leisure Park, Churchill Way West, Basingstoke, Hampshire RG22 6PG The Museum's collection includes recreated historic streets and shops, vintage vehicles, the Thornycroft Collection, trams, agricultural machinery and an Edwardian pub. Open Tuesday to Sunday and Bank Holidays. Admission charge.

MOSI Manchester
www.msimanchester.org.uk tel: 0161 832 2244 Liverpool Road, Castlefield, Manchester, M3 4FP The Museum of Science & Industry is housed in five listed buildings including Liverpool Road Station, the world's first passenger station. It covers a wide range of themes focusing on Manchester's contribution to science and industry. The 'Transport Revolutions' collection in the Air & Space Hall contains several examples of early Manchester-built motor cars. Open daily. Free admission.

Myreton Motor Museum
www.myretonmotormuseum.co.uk tel: 01875 870288 Aberlady, East Lothian, EH32 0PZ A collection of cars – including some rare Scottish-built vehicles – bicycles, motor cycles and commercial vehicles from 1899-1989, period advertising, posters, enamel signs, and toy vehicles. Open daily. Admission charge.

National Motor Museum Beaulieu
www.beaulieu.co.uk/attractions/national-motor-museum tel: 01590 612345 Brockenhurst, Hampshire, United Kingdom, SO42 7ZN Housing a collection of over 250 automobiles and motorcycles the museum tells the story of motoring on the roads of Britain from the earliest days to the present time. The admission charge covers entrance to the National Motor Museum, Palace House and Gardens, Beaulieu Abbey and the World of Top Gear. Open daily. Admission charge.

Trolley Bus Museum
www.sandtoft.org tel: 01724 711391 Belton Road, Sandtoft, Doncaster, DN8 5SX Home to the largest collection of trolleybuses in the UK, this fascinating museum also houses a collection of motor buses and assorted vehicles associated with the maintenance of overhead power lines. It is only open on specific events days, so check website for details.

INDEX